W9-CPJ-132

THE J.F.K. ASSASSINATION QUIZ BOOK

TEST YOUR KNOWLEDGE

by Walt Brown, Ph.D.

Foreword by

Cyril H. Wecht, M.D., J.D. and Gary L. Aguilar, M.D.

Open Archive Press
P.O. Box 23511
Santa Barbara, CA 93121

THE J.F.K. ASSASSINATION QUIZ BOOK

TEST YOUR KNOWLEDGE

by Walt Brown, Ph.D

Published by

Open Archive Press

P.O. Box 23511

Santa Barbara, CA 93121

Telephone (805) 899-3433

FAX (805) 899-4773

ISBN: 0-9636380-1-7

This work is dedicated in loving memory to
Raymond Povinelli
(1923-1994)
whose innate sense of curiosity was an inspiration
for this work, and whose loss was greater
than the one I sustained on November 22, 1963.

FOREWORD

While quite a broad range of authors with varying levels of expertise have written on the subject of the Kennedy assassination, there are at most literally a handful of individuals who know the primary source materials as thoroughly as Walt Brown, the admired author of The People v. Lee Harvey Oswald. It is likely that no one knows the content of the Warren Commission Report and its volumes better than Walt Brown - not even, or perhaps one should say especially not the remaining living members of the Warren Commission itself. His breadth of expertise extends well beyond the specific content of the Warren data, however, and Brown brings to his scrutiny of JFK's death a formidable intellect. Respected by all, Walt Brown has been aptly described as the "experts' expert."

Brown has taught and written on the subject of the Kennedy assassination for many years. As a teacher with superb academic credentials, he knows the importance of education in any field, including the subject of JFK's death. He also knows the value of the Socratic method — teaching done more through asking than answering, rather than by simply laying out information as if on a banquet table to be quickly ingested, and, as often happens, just as quickly eliminated. The challenge of a question engages the mind, and especially if one is at first stumped, the final discovery of the answer leads to a better retention and integration of the information. Brown uses Socrates to great advantage in his new book. Though such an approach has much value on the JFK subject, the infinite variety of possible questions does not lend itself to an easy selection of pivotal and illustrative queries. Happily, Brown's experience as a teacher and his mastery of the subject have been conjoined to produce an enlightening list of fascinating questions of interest and value to both JFK novices and experts alike. However, the reader must be forewarned; studying Brown's list will be at once both as humbling an experience as it is an enjoyably edifying one, even for those of us who, before gazing upon Brown's compilation, thought we knew something about John Kennedy's assassination.

Cyril H. Wecht, MD, JD
Chairman, Department of Pathology, St. Francis Central Hospital, Pittsburgh, Pennsylvania
Past President, American Academy of Forensic Sciences
Adjunct Professor of Law, Duquesne University

AND

Gary L. Aguilar, MD
Chairman, Department of Surgery, Saint Francis Memorial Hospital, San Francisco
Assistant Professor of Ophthalmology, Stanford University Medical Center
Assistant Professor of Ophthalmology, University of California, San Francisco

AUTHOR'S INTRODUCTION

It is no secret that there are many *unanswered* questions about the tragedy which occurred in Dealey Plaza at approximately 12:30 PM Central Standard Time on November 22, 1963. The vast majority of those unknown questions continue to trouble researchers, concerned citizens who read the findings of the researchers, at least 90% of the American population, and millions of people worldwide, who loved the thirty-fifth President, and who believe that John F. Kennedy's life was ended as a result of a conspiracy.

An equally great concern, given the magnitude of the case, is the ease with which a rumor or theory suddenly becomes fact. A careless sentence at a seminar or an unsubstantiated fact in a book suddenly becomes "public domain" and is trumpeted worldwide as *proof* of one of many conspiracy theories. Regrettably, such errors then become the bases for further misunderstanding, and instead of heading toward Pierre Teilhard de Chardin's "point of omega" with respect to the assassination, we are still diverging and making the task of arriving at the truth all the more difficult and frustrating.

Yet even thirty-plus years after the assassination, hard knowledge of the event is to a great extent not widely disseminated. Having written books and articles on the Kennedy assassination, I have had many opportunities to meet a great many Americans—as well as people from all corners of the globe—who have questions about the case, and I answer them as well as I can, although, at the risk of disappointing an occasional listener, I try to stick to the facts and to steer the audience in the same direction. As time has passed, my audiences have grown, and so too has their appreciation that we must deal from facts.

This explains both the clamor for release of existing files and for this book. While this book certainly makes no pretense to be a substitute for

This explains both the clamor for release of existing files and for this book. While this book certainly makes no pretense to be a substitute for the hundreds of thousands of as-yet unreleased documents, it is intended to provide its readers with facts in the case—not opinions, and it is hoped that those facts will do two things. First, it will give the reader of this book a good grounding in the essentials of the events of November 22, 1963. After all, we do know the where and the when; we continue to seek the who, how, and, perhaps most importantly, the why. Secondly, it is presented in this specific format as a challenge to the reader. It could have just as easily been done as "1,000 Facts About the Assassination," but in such form its readers would have given it the once-over and concluded, "Oh, I knew that stuff," and moved on.

Unfortunately, the above quotation would not be accurate. For that reason, I have chosen to ask the reader 1,000 questions about the assassination and let the reader decide, as he or she twists and turns through perhaps the six most crucial seconds of the Twentieth Century, if, in fact, they do know the facts. If they do not, the message to them is obvious: Go back and read additional material and do not fear to be critical if future reading runs afoul of what we know to be the facts.

CAVEAT EMPTOR:

This book is not intended as a game in which the reader scores points based on knowledge of the event. To do that would be to demean even further the luster of Camelot that has been tarnished enough by recent revelations. In writing this book, the author confronted an obvious but little-discussed irony: The two most common "time-frames" used to refer to John Kennedy's presidency are "A Thousand Days" and "Six Seconds in Dallas." Yet there are perhaps only six decent books about the thousand days, and a thousand books about the six seconds. Much of the data regarding the thousand days are well researched and scholarly; an indecent percent of the "six seconds" books are not as well researched, often confuse speculation with fact, and bombast with rhetoric.

This book contains 1,000 questions, divided (not necessarily perfectly) into categories of "Beginner," "Intermediate," and "Expert." It had its origins in the summer of 1993, when two events so close in time demanded that a review of facts be undertaken, and in a way that would challenge the reader's knowledge, not pretend to inflate it. During the summer of 1993, I taught a college course on the Kennedy Assassination in New Jersey. I had 42 bright, eager students, but many suffered from the defects that this book hopes to correct. At the same time, my wife was proofreading chapters from an upcoming assassination book, and having read a chapter, she asked me to "quiz her" on what she had read. For her, it was to determine if she had read for content or for typing errors, and she wanted to learn what she had taken away, content-wise, from her reading. I asked about a dozen questions (and she did quite well), and it suddenly occurred to me that the vast number of people who still care enough about the memory of John F. Kennedy that they want the truth to emerge sooner or later would find such questions of equal interest, and they would be richer for the experience. For any reader who can claim to know the vast majority of the answers to the questions contained herein, you should begin your own area of research and put your expertise to work. For those who learn a great deal from this book (and I suspect there will be many), it is hoped that you will continue your reading and your learning so that someday you, too, can contribute to the literature.

It is also hoped that someday the full truth emerges so that many Americans who are still so concerned about those terrible six seconds and who, like this author, had a piece of them die that day in Dealey Plaza can move on to the many, many other serious concerns that face the entire human race today. Let us seek the answers together.

Walt Brown
July 1995

JFK—BEGINNER

1. In what state was John F. Kennedy born?

2. When was Kennedy born?

3. Of the nine children born to Joe Sr. and Rose Kennedy, which one, in order, was JFK?

4. In what state did JFK spend much of his childhood?

5. What boarding school did JFK attend?

6. Where did JFK begin his college education?

7. Where did Kennedy complete his undergraduate work?

8. Where in the U.S. did Kennedy do graduate studies?

9. Where outside the U.S. did Kennedy have a brief period of graduate studies?

10. What was the major concern regarding JFK during his university days?

Answers on next page

ANSWERS
JFK—BEGINNER

1. Massachusetts.

2. May 29, 1917.

3. Second oldest, behind Joe Jr.

4. New York, specifically the Riverdale section of the Bronx, New York City.

5. Choate.

6. Princeton.

7. Harvard.

8. Stanford.

9. London School of Economics.

10. His deteriorating health.

JFK—BEGINNER II

1. Kennedy devoted much work to his senior thesis in college. What was its title?

2. Kennedy accompanied his father to what country, where Joe Sr. was the U.S. ambassador?

3. What American seemed the most militant against Joe Sr. holding that ambassador's post?

4. Which of the other Kennedy "children" were nearby in Europe while JFK was there?

5. What were Kennedy's military duties prior to being transferred to the South Pacific?

6. What agency had tape recordings that were instrumental in causing the transfer to the South Pacific?

7. What was the name of JFK's boat?

8. How did JFK conclude his military career?

9. When did JFK first run for Congress?

10. What other future political leader entered Congress at the same time as Kennedy?

Answers on next page

ANSWERS
JFK—BEGINNER II

1. *Why England Slept*.

2. England.

3. Eleanor Roosevelt; FDR tolerated him.

4. Joe Jr. and Kathleen were also in England during some of JFK's time there.

5. Desk work — Office of Naval Intelligence (ONI).

6. FBI.

7. PT-109.

8. He was land-based, working on ways to better arm PT-boats, as well as training future crews.

9. 1946.

10. Richard Nixon.

JFK—INTERMEDIATE

1. Who managed virtually all of JFK's political campaigns?

2. What is the commonly accepted theory of why JFK became the political leader among the Kennedy youth?

3. What was Kennedy's one and only non-governmental job?

4. Who was the "Nazi sympathizer" with whom JFK had a relationship that led, in part, to his transfer to the South Pacific?

5. What did Kennedy do with his government paychecks as well as his publishing royalties?

6. On what part of his anatomy did Kennedy have surgery performed?

7. How successful was the surgery?

8. How ill was Kennedy at the time of the surgery?

9. What disease clearly did not help Kennedy remain healthy?

10. When did Kennedy marry Jacqueline Bouvier?

Answers on next page

ANSWERS
JFK—INTERMEDIATE

1. Robert Kennedy.

2. The commonly accepted answer is the death of older brother Joe; but Joe's abrasive personality, like Joe Sr., might ultimately have put JFK in the limelight regardless.

3. Journalist — he covered post-war Europe and the opening of the U.N.

4. Inga Arvad.

5. Those monies were donated to charity.

6. His lower back.

7. The surgery was not very successful.

8. Very ill; he received the last rites of the Roman Catholic Church twice in the mid-50s.

9. Addison's disease.

10. September 12, 1953. They were married ten years, two months, and ten days.

JFK—INTERMEDIATE II

1. Where was the Kennedy family winter residence located?

2. Where did JFK spend election night in 1960?

3. What praise did JFK heap on LBJ at the Democratic convention?

4. When did Kennedy realize he had been elected President?

5. Whom did Kennedy defeat to win a seat in the Senate?

6. How did Kennedy vote on the question of censuring Joe McCarthy?

7. What office did Kennedy seek in 1956?

8. Who eventually got it?

9. When did Kennedy's campaign for President unofficially begin?

10. By 1960, how many of the remaining Kennedy "children" would be available to campaign for JFK?

Answers on next page

ANSWERS
JFK—INTERMEDIATE II

1. Palm Beach, Florida.

2. Hyannis Port.

3. He highly praised Johnson's work as Senate Majority Leader, kidding the audience that LBJ was so good at that job that he should stay there.

4. When he awoke the morning after the election, Secret Service agents were patrolling the Hyannis Port grounds; JFK had gone to sleep before the results were final.

5. Henry Cabot Lodge. (Nixon's V.P. candidate in '60.)

6. He did not vote; some saw this as politically-oriented fence-sitting.

7. Vice-President on the Democratic ticket.

8. The Democrats nominated Estes Kefauver, but Nixon remained as V.P.

9. As soon as the election of 1956 ended, for all purposes.

10. Five; Joe and Kathleen were deceased and Rosemary was institutionalized; excluding JFK, five were left.

JFK—EXPERT

1. What two sports did the young JFK actively pursue?

2. How did Joseph Kennedy Jr. die?

3. How did JFK's sister Kathleen spend the last years of her life?

4. What tragedy befell Kennedy's sister Rosemary?

5. What was the one business that Joe Kennedy Sr. failed at?

6. How did Kennedy explain his hero status after World War II?

7. Name JFK's private airplane, used extensively for campaigning.

8. What pollster did Kennedy hire to take samplings full-time and provide non-stop political information?

9. What "symbolic" gift did JFK accept half-heartedly on November 22?

10. Where was Kennedy eight days before Germany initiated World War II by attacking Poland?

Answers on next page

ANSWER
JFK—EXPERT

1. Football and swimming.

2. In an ill-conceived bombing mission in a plane loaded with high explosives; the radar-controlled plane exploded and disintegrated and Joe Jr. was never found.

3. Kathleen married into English royalty during World War II, only to have her husband killed in the war; she remained in England for the most part and died in a 1948 plane crash.

4. She was retarded; her parents decided on surgery and the subsequent lobotomy did not help her at all.

5. The motion picture industry, although the work did have its "perks."

6. He told audiences, "They sank my boat."

7. The *Caroline*.

8. Louis Harris.

9. A ten-gallon Texan hat, which he refused to put on.

10. In Poland, being the eyes and ears of his father, Ambassador Kennedy.

JFK—EXPERT II

1. What was the subject of Kennedy's second book?

2. What rumor did LBJ float regarding Kennedy's nomination in 1960?

3. What was the first primary that Kennedy entered in 1960?

4. Which primary was the most challenging?

5. How many primaries did Kennedy enter in the 1960 campaign?

6. Of those, how many did he win?

7. What state's delegate count gave Kennedy the Presidential nomination?

8. On what ballot was Kennedy nominated?

9. In which of the four debates did the candidates not face each other?

10. What were the two key states on election day?

Answers on next page

ANSWERS
JFK EXPERT II

1. The death of Joe Jr. It was a book of remembrances put together by JFK from those who knew Joe best. It then was published in a private print run of 350 copies.

2. That JFK would not live out his term because of his illness; LBJ was half-right.

3. Wisconsin.

4. West Virginia.

5. Five.

6. He won all five he entered.

7. Wyoming.

8. The first.

9. The third debate.

10. Texas and Illinois; had they gone to Nixon, he would have been elected.

JFK—INTERMEDIATE III

1. What book did Kennedy write while recovering from surgery?

2. Name the mafia-connected woman who had regular liaisons with Kennedy, sometimes in the White House.

3. Who introduced Kennedy to her?

4. Name the Kennedy child who died within days of his birth in 1963.

5. What poet was invited to give a poetry reading at the 1961 inauguration?

6. What journalist covered both the Kennedy and Nixon campaigns in 1960 and would go on to write books about political campaigns every four years?

7. What did Kennedy tell Walter Cronkite in a televised interview about Vietnam in September 1963?

8. What was the major foreign policy success for Kennedy in 1963?

9. What event, according to Ted Sorenson, did Kennedy dismiss with the comment that it would be quickly forgotten?

10. Again, according to Sorenson, what event did Kennedy depict as the biggest day he would ever have in his life?

Answers on next page

ANSWERS
JFK—INTERMEDIATE III

1. *Profiles in Courage.*

2. Judith Campbell (later Exner).

3. Frank Sinatra.

4. Patrick Bouvier Kennedy.

5. Robert Frost.

6. Theodore White.

7. "In the final analysis, it's their war" (and they have to win it).

8. Test-ban Treaty.

9. The successful end of the Cuban Missile Crisis.

10. The day of the "Ich bin ein Berliner" speech.

JFK—INTERMEDIATE IV

1. What three prominent individuals left their jobs at the CIA following the Bay of Pigs fiasco in 1961?

2. What previously learned skill helped make Kennedy a war hero in the South Pacific?

3. What reminder of that event did Kennedy have on his desk in the White House?

4. What phrase has been used to describe the advisors that Kennedy surrounded himself with?

5. What "space" related gift did Kennedy receive from Khrushchev?

6. What civil rights leader did candidate Kennedy attempt to "protect" during the 1960 campaign, and what results did the action have?

7. When the steel crisis occurred, how much was the price of steel raised?

8. At which college did Kennedy give a speech in 1963 which would suggest the tone of his future policies?

9. What phrase from that speech is a title of a Kennedy assassination book?

10. How long did the Cuban Missile Crisis last for those who were privy to the entire process?

Answers on next page

ANSWERS
JFK—INTERMEDIATE IV

1. Allan Dulles, Richard Bissell, and General Charles Cabell.

2. Swimming.

3. The coconut on which he carved a message.

4. "The best and the brightest."

5. JFK received a dog from a litter of pups born to a Russian space dog.

6. Martin Luther King; almost overnight, the Black vote swung heavily to Kennedy; King's father had planned to vote for Nixon, but changed his mind. Kennedy would get 78% of the Black vote.

7. $6 per ton.

8. American University in Washington, D.C.

9. *And We Are All Mortal*. (Book by scholar George Michael Evica.)

10. Thirteen days, later memorialized in a book by RFK, and put on silver desk plaques for those advisors who were there.

JFK—EXPERT III

1. With what steel-company executive did Kennedy have the most contact during the "steel" crisis?

2. What cabinet member was also prominent in the settlement of the problems with the steel industry?

3. What was the name of Caroline's pony?

4. Who was the Brigade leader in the Bay of Pigs?

5. What did the group call itself?

6. What U.S. Senator had spoken often of a Cuban missile threat well before the October 1962 crisis?

7. After the inaugural parties on the night of January 20, 1961, where is Kennedy reputed to have gone?

8. What were Kennedy's first duties after his recovery from his heroic events in the South Pacific?

9. What song did Marilyn Monroe sing to Kennedy?

10. How many times did the Dallas motorcade stop at Kennedy's insistence?

Answers on next page

ANSWERS
JFK—EXPERT III

1. Roger Blough.

2. Secretary of Labor Arthur Goldberg.

3. Macaroni.

4. Manuel Artime.

5. Brigade 2506.

6. Kenneth Keating of New York.

7. To columnist Joseph Alsop's house, where some believe he carried on an extra-marital affair. Mrs. Kennedy was already asleep in the White House, resting after giving birth in November to John Jr.

8. He trained other crews and attempted to place stronger armaments and armor plating on the weak and otherwise ill-equipped PT boats.

9. "Happy Birthday."

10. Twice. After the shooting, the car passed Chief Curry's car, and then had to stop to find the way to the hospital.

JFK IN LIFE & POLITICS—BEGINNER

1. Where did JFK get married?

2. How many Presidents are buried in Washington, D.C?

3. What other President is buried in Arlington National Cemetery?

4. For which book did JFK receive the Pulitzer Prize?

5. Did any other Presidents prior to 1963 win the Pulitzer Prize?

6. How many other Presidents had appointed a brother to the Cabinet?

7. To what amount was the minimum wage raised in 1961?

8. Who was the first American astronaut launched?

9. How many Presidents have died in office?

10. What were Caroline Kennedy and Patrick Kennedy's middle name?

Answers on next page

ANSWERS
JFK IN LIFE & POLITICS—BEGINNER

1. Newport, Rhode Island.

2. One; Woodrow Wilson, at the National Cathedral. (Sorry for the trick question; JFK is buried in Arlington, in Virginia.)

3. William Howard Taft.

4. *Profiles in Courage*.

5. No — only JFK.

6. None and, fortunately, neither Jimmy Carter nor Bill Clinton continued the tradition. Woodrow Wilson approinted a Wilson, but no relation.

7. $1.15 per hour.

8. Alan Shepard, May 5, 1961, three weeks after the Russians finally brought one back alive.

9. Eight.

10. Bouvier.

JFK IN LIFE AND POLITICS—INTERMEDIATE

1. Where was Kennedy born?

2. How many Presidents were born in the same state as Kennedy?

3. What did JFK receive on May 29, 1938?

4. How many other Presidents wrote books that were published in their lifetimes?

5. How many Presidents served in the U.S. Navy?

6. How many Presidents served in World War II?

7. How many states did JFK carry in the 1960 election (out of a possible 50)?

8. What did JFK do with his Presidential salary?

9. What other President did likewise with his Presidential salary?

10. What political group did Kennedy condemn as 'totally alien' to American politics?

Answers on next page

ANSWERS
JFK IN LIFE & POLITICS—INTERMEDIATE

1. 83 Beals Street, Brookline, Massachusetts.

2. Three others: John Adams, John Quincy Adams and George Bush.

3. On his twenty-first birthday, Kennedy received a trust fund of one million dollars. (An incalculable amount in today's bucks...)

4. Nineteen other Presidents before JFK were published in their lifetimes.

5. Three.

6. Kennedy was the second President elected with World War II service; Eisenhower, then JFK; LBJ served briefly; Nixon, Ford, Carter, and Bush also saw service.

7. Twenty-two, and five electors from Alabama.

8. He donated it to charity.

9. Herbert Hoover.

10. The John Birch Society.

JFK IN LIFE AND POLITICS—EXPERT

1. Kennedy was one of two Presidents survived by his father. Who was the other?

2. Kennedy was also survived by his mother. How many other Presidents were survived by their mothers?

3. How many Presidents were survived by both parents?

4. How many other first ladies remarried?

5. What Japanese boat rammed *PT-109*?

6. How many previous Presidents had been members of the House of Representatives?

7. How many previous Presidents had served in the Senate?

8. How many previous Presidents had served in both the House and the Senate?

9. How many Presidents, up to and including Kennedy, had been elected President with less than 50% of the popular vote?

10. What was unique about JFK's first press conference?

Answers on next page

ANSWERS
JFK IN LIFE AND POLITICS—EXPERT

1. Warren G. Harding.

2. Two other Presidents were survived by their mothers.

3. Only one — JFK.

4. One — Francis Cleveland, nee Folsom. Of course, the widow Cleveland had married Grover when she was 21 and he was 49. She remarried at age 48; Jackie married JFK at age 23 and remarried when she was 39.

5. The *Amagiri*.

6. Fifteen previous Presidents had served in Congress.

7. Thirteen previous Presidents had served in the Senate.

8. Eight previous Presidents had served in both the House and Senate.

9. Kennedy was the fourteenth to be elected with less than 50% of the popular vote total.

10. It was the first press conference televised live and had an estimated audience of fifty to sixty million viewers.

JFK IN LIFE AND POLITICS—EXPERT+

1. How many Presidents came from families of nine children?

2. Approximately how much deficit was in Kennedy's first budget?

3. What amendment was ratified during JFK's first year in office and what did it involve?

4. What was the Peace Corps' first project?

5. Up to and including JFK, how many Presidents had traveled outside the United States while in office?

6. How many vetoes did Kennedy use?

7. Of that total, how many vetoes were subsequently overridden?

8. What famous world leader did Kennedy proclaim as an honorary U.S. citizen?

9. Up to and including Kennedy, how many Presidents had met with the Pope while in office?

10. How many Presidents besides JFK lost children while in office?

Answers on next page

ANSWERS
JFK IN LIFE & POLITICS—EXPERT+

1. Seven.

2. Two billion, one hundred sixty-nine million dollars.

3. The Twenty-third; it allowed residents of the District of Columbia to vote for Presidential electors.

4. Construction of a road in Tanganyika.

5. Only nine.

6. Twenty-one. The last one was used on November 19, 1963.

7. None.

8. Winston Churchill.

9. Nine. The pope had visited Woodrow Wilson and FDR here in America.

10. Four others, the most notable being Lincoln, and perhaps the saddest was the loss of Franklin Pierce's son in a train wreck while Pierce and his family were going to Washington to be sworn in. The young boy was the only fatality on the train. Pierce's other two children died in infancy.

JFK'S LIMOUSINE—EXPERT

1. Besides its protective capacity, what was different about the car with the top off?

2. Does the car still exist today, and if so, where?

3. Where was the vehicle registered, and what were the plate numbers?

4. What other President used the car the President was riding in when shot?

5. How long did Texas authorities spend checking the car for evidence?

6. What part of the limousine was permanently removed and retained as evidence?

7. Where were bullet fragments found in the car?

8. Where did the car exhibit damage from bullets?

9. Which of the wounded occupants of the car was removed first?

10. After the car was returned to Washington and was searched, what happened to it?

Answers on next page

ANSWERS
JFK'S LIMOUSINE—EXPERT

1. The back seat could not be raised or lowered when the top was off.

2. The car is on display in Dearborn, Michigan, in a Ford museum.

3. The car was registered in D.C. The plates were GG-300.

4. Technically, no President; it was new for JFK and rebuilt for use of subsequent Presidents.

5. No time. It was spirited away from Parkland Hospital in haste.

6. The windshield.

7. Two larger fragments were found in the front seat; smaller fragments were found under the carpeting by Mrs. Connally's jump seat.

8. In the windshield and in the chrome that framed the windshield.

9. Governor Connally, as he was blocking JFK's way and Mrs. Kennedy was still cradling the President, unwilling to release him to medical personnel for no purpose.

10. Carl Renas, a Ford employee, drove the car from D.C. to Cincinnati, with a helicopter escort all the way. The car was then totally rebuilt, and painted black (per LBJ), instead of "Kennedy blue."

TEXAS SCHOOL BOOK DEPOSITORY—INTERMEDIATE

1. On what corner is the Book Depository located?

2. How many floors does the Depository contain?

3. How many elevators were in the TSBD on November 22, 1963?

4. Who was the manager of the Depository on November 22, 1963?

5. Which floor was receiving new floor boards on November 22, 1963?

6. On which floor was the lunch room located?

7. On which floors were the textbooks kept?

8. What company advertised on the sign on the roof of the Depository?

9. What is the former Texas School Book Depository today?

10. What standard tourist item is strictly prohibited in the former
    Book Depository?

Answers on next page

ANSWERS
TEXAS SCHOOL BOOK DEPOSITORY—INTERMEDIATE

1. The northwest corner of Houston Street and Elm Street.

2. Seven.

3. Three; two that carried freight and serviced all floors, and one for passengers that only serviced the lower floors.

4. Roy Truly.

5. The sixth floor.

6. The second floor; there was a "rec" room on the first floor where some employees occasionally ate.

7. Primarily the fifth and sixth, although there were some bins on the first floor as well.

8. Hertz.

9. It is a publicly owned building, with no access to any floor except the sixth, which is a strictly kept and security conscious museum reached by elevator for a fee of $6.

10. Cameras.

TEXAS SCHOOL BOOK DEPOSITORY—EXPERT

1. Who found the three spent cartridges on the sixth floor?

2. What other items were found near the "sniper's nest"?

3. Who placed the boxes of books around the sniper's nest?

4. How much did the average carton of books weigh?

5. What was the address of the Texas School Book Depository?

6. Who admitted to bringing a Mauser rifle into the Depository two days before the Presidential motorcade?

7. Which two individuals simultaneously noticed the concealed rifle?

8. Who was the crime lab chief on the scene at the TSBD?

9. Who was his assistant?

10. Who found Oswald's clipboard and when?

Answers on next page

ANSWERS
TEXAS SCHOOL BOOK DEPOSITORY—EXPERT

1. Luke Mooney.

2. A bag, believed to have held the rifle, a smaller bag with chicken remains, a pop bottle, and a cigarette pack.

3. The crew that was doing the flooring work on the sixth floor.

4. 55 pounds.

5. 411 Elm Street.

6. Warren Caster, TSBD employee.

7. Eugene Boone and Seymour Weitzman.

8. Lt. Carl Day.

9. Robert Studebaker.

10. Frankie Kaiser found the clipboard on December 2, 1963.

GUNS—INTERMEDIATE

1. What was the serial number of Oswald's Mannlicher-Carcano?

2. What was the Warren Commission's exhibit number for Oswald's Mannlicher-Carcano?

3. Did the Mannlicher-Carcano come delivered with an ammunition clip?

4. How many shots could the Mannlicher-Carcano fire with one clip?

5. How many rounds were in the Mannlicher-Carcano when it was found by Dallas authorities?

6. Was there anything unusual about the telescopic sight on the Mannlicher-Carcano found at the TSBD?

7. Did the Mannlicher-Carcano found at the TSBD test out as an accurate weapon?

8. Oswald is only known to have seriously discussed guns with one person during the year 1963. Identify that person.

9. From what source did Oswald purchase the Mannlicher-Carcano?

10. Where was the Mannlicher-Carcano alleged to have been during most of September, October, and November of 1963?

Answers on next page

ANSWERS
GUNS—INTERMEDIATE

1. C2766. The "Oswald gun" was not, however, the only Mannlicher made with that serial number.

2. CE 139.

3. No.

4. Six from the clip, but an additional bullet could already be chambered.

5. One.

6. It was sighted for a left-handed shooter, according to an FBI document. It would be more accurate to say that the rifle's configuration did not in fact allow for a scope to be mounted, so it had to be jerry-rigged on the left-hand side.

7. No. The scope needed shims for adjustment and still fired high and to the right.

8. Adrian Alba.

9. Klein's Sporting Goods in Chicago.

10. In a blanket in the garage at the Paine residence in Irving, Texas.

GUNS—EXPERT

1. What peculiarity was common to both Oswald's rifle and his pistol?

2. What police officer's family, years later, would suddenly be in possession of a different backyard photo?

3. What was the total price, including shipping, of Oswald's rifle?

4. What was the difference in size between the rifle Oswald ordered and the one he received?

5. When taken apart, how large is the wooden stock of Oswald's rifle?

6. Could there have existed another Mannlicher-Carcano rifle with the identical serial number?

7. In the searches conducted at the Paine residence and the boarding house at 1026 N. Beckley, what gun-related items were found?

8. What type of gun did the Secret Service agent brandish shortly after the shooting?

9. To test the Carcano's ability to penetrate ribs, what was it tested on?

10. What was the original caliber of Mannlicher-Carcano rifles?

Answers on next page

ANSWERS
GUNS—EXPERT

1. Both weapons had different barrels than were originally designed for the respective weapons.

2. Roscoe White.

3. $21.45.

4. 4 inches.

5. Just under 36 inches.

6. Yes; several factories were manufacturing them.

7. No rifle related materials at all; a holster for the pistol was found at the boarding house at 1026 N. Beckley. It seems odd for someone to have left behind pictures of himself with a rifle, yet sanitized the place with respect to gun cleaning tools or oil.

8. An Ar-15 rifle.

9. Anesthetized goats.

10. 7.35 mm.

BALLISTICS—INTERMEDIATE

1. Indicate the size (caliber) of the bullets fired by a Mannlicher-Carcano rifle.

2. Give the size (caliber) of bullets fired by a German Mauser.

3. What was the size, as measured at autopsy, of President Kennedy's back wound?

4. What was the size, as measured at autopsy, of the supposed entry wound in Kennedy's skull?

5. What was the angle from the President to the sixth-floor window of the Texas School Book Depository?

6. What was the angle, according to the autopsists, of the Kennedy back wound?

7. What was the angle, according to the Warren Commission, of the wound through President Kennedy's neck?

8. What was the angle of the wound, as indicated by attending physicians, of Governor Connally's wound?

9. At what speed did a bullet from a Mannlicher-Carcano rifle travel?

10. Given the speed in question 9, does that make it a "high-powered rifle"?

Answers on next page

ANSWER
BALLISTICS—INTERMEDIATE

1. 6.5 mm.

2. 7.65 mm.

3. 7 x 4 mm.

4. 15 x 6 mm.

5. 21 degrees when measured in the horizontal plane; 69 degrees in the vertical plane.

6. 45 degrees.

7. 11 degrees.

8. 39 degrees.

9. 2,160 feet per second.

10. No. High-powered rifles will fire projectiles at up to 4,000 feet per second.

THE MAGIC BULLET—INTERMEDIATE

1. What is the Commission's designation for the magic bullet?

2. What was the weight of the bullet with respect to the normal weight of a similar bullet?

3. Who found the magic bullet?

4. Who handled the bullet second?

5. Which agency initially refused to accept custody of the bullet?

6. To whom was the bullet then given?

7. Who ultimately gave the bullet to the FBI?

8. What did the Dallas authorities have to do with the magic bullet?

9. On whose stretcher was the magic bullet found?

10. What was the most sophisticated test performed on the bullet?

Answers on next page

ANSWERS:
MAGIC BULLET—INTERMEDIATE

1. CE 399.

2. CE 399 weighed 158.6 grains; normal weight is 161 grains. (437.5 grains is one ounce; hence, 2.4/437.5 or 54 ten-thousandths of an ounce was missing.)

3. Darrell Tomlinson.

4. Parkland security man O.P. Wright.

5. FBI.

6. Special Agent Richard Johnsen of the Secret Service.

7. James Rowley, Secret Service Chief.

8. They never saw it.

9. Darrell Tomlinson was not sure; The Warren Commission insisted that Tomlinson found it on Connally's stretcher.

10. Neutron Activation Analysis.

NEW ORLEANS INTRIGUE—INTERMEDIATE

1. For whom did Oswald work while in New Orleans?

2. With what New Orleans attorney did Oswald consult during the summer of 1963?

3. What former ONI and FBI agent had offices at 531 Lafayette Street, which was also entered through 544 Camp Street?

4. What literature was stamped with that address?

5. What other individual of far-right politics operated out of 544 Camp Street?

6. Who was the District Attorney of New Orleans in 1963?

7. How many members were in the New Orleans chapter of the FPCC?

8. Whose business had been visited by Oswald a few days before the "leaflet fracas"?

9. What New Orleans businessman was arrested in 1967 and charged with the murder of JFK?

10. What other New Orleans individual, seen as having strong mob influence, is also mentioned with respect to the JFK killing?

Answers on next page

ANSWERS
NEW ORLEANS INTRIGUE—INTERMEDIATE

1. William B. Reily Coffee Company.

2. Dean Andrews.

3. Guy Banister.

4. Some of Oswald's FPCC literature bore "544 Camp Street".

5. David Ferrie; Sergio Arcacha-Smith;

6. Jim Garrison.

7. One — Lee Oswald.

8. Carlos Bringuier's business.

9. Clay Shaw.

10. Carlos Marcello.

NEW ORLEANS INTRIGUE—EXPERT

1. Where did Oswald live in New Orleans?

2. What New Orleans relative of Oswald's is often seen as an organized crime employee?

3. Who was the private eye working at 544 Camp Street who was pistol whipped on November 22?

4. What police officer recorded Clay Shaw's admitted alias?

5. Whom did Oswald pay $2 to hand out leaflets for fifteen minutes?

6. Who told Louisiana authorities in advance that JFK would be killed?

7. What FBI man interviewed Oswald in New Orleans?

8. Who handled most of the prosecution's case in the Shaw trial?

9. Who was the prosecution's key witness in the Shaw trial?

10. What was Jim Garrison's name at birth?

Answers on next page

ANSWERS
NEW ORLEANS INTRIGUE—EXPERT

1. 4907 Magazine Street.

2. Charles "Dutz" Murret.

3. Jack Martin.

4. Aloysius Habighorst.

5. Charles Steele, Jr. He testified before the Warren Commission about the event; the next witness was Charles Steele, Sr., who testified that Charlie Jr. was essentially a well-behaved tyke.

6. Rose Cheramie. (She is seen being thrown from a moving car at the beginning of *JFK*.)

7. John Quigley.

8. Andrew ("Moo Moo") Sciambra.

9. Perry Russo.

10. Earling Carothers Garrison.

DEALEY PLAZA—INTERMEDIATE

1. For whom was Dealey Plaza named, and what was the noteworthy nature of that person's life?

2. Prior to November 22, 1963, what was the historical significance of Dealey Plaza?

3. How big is Dealey Plaza?

4. Which three streets go through Dealey Plaza?

5. When was the Triple Underpass constructed?

6. What was the original name of the brick building on the north end of Dealey Plaza?

7. What other President had had a motorcade through Dealey Plaza?

8. From Houston Street, what is the downward slope of Dealey Plaza?

9. Parking behind the picket fence at the north end of Dealey Plaza was reserved for whom?

10. What two "official" buildings overlooked Dealey Plaza on November 22, 1963?

Answers on next page

ANSWERS
DEALEY PLAZA—INTERMEDIATE

1. George Bannerman Dealey; turn-of-the-century Dallas newspaper editor.

2. It was the site of the first house built in Dallas.

3. 3.07 acres is the size usually cited; when it became a historical landmark on November 22, 1993, dignitaries were quick to thank those who had donated land or property, suggesting that the historical plaza may be slightly larger.

4. Elm Street extension (sometimes called "Parkway"), Main Street, and Commerce Street.

5. 1936. Warren Commission Exhibits exhaustively prove this.
   God knows why.

6. The Sexton Building. It is cited as such in a few Warren Commission exhibits that would be damaging to the official version if listed as the TSBD.

7. Franklin D. Roosevelt, the first Presidential detail that Dallas agent Forrest Sorrels was part of; unlike JFK's motorcade, Roosevelt went west to east through Dealey Plaza—and survived.

8. 3 degrees.

9. The sheriff's department and other county employees.

10. The County Jail and the County Records Building.

MOTORCADE—INTERMEDIATE

1. Precisely which position (numerically) did the Presidential limousine occupy in the November 22 motorcade?

2. What direction was JFK's car going at the time of the shooting?

3. The Zapruder film indicated the motorcade was travelling at what speed during the sequence of shots?

4. The shooting occured on what street in Dealey Plaza?

5. What color was the Presidential limousine?

6. What three vehicles were behind the Presidential limousine?

7. How far was the President's car from the "sniper's window" at the time of the fatal shot?

8. After the shooting, did the entire motorcade proceed to Parkland Hospital?

9. What highway did the motorcade access immediately after the shooting?

10. How many open windows were estimated on the motorcade route?

Answers on next page

ANSWERS
MOTORCADE—INTERMEDIATE

1. Kennedy's car was third, behind a pilot car a quarter of a mile ahead and a lead car approximately forty yards ahead.

2. West (slightly by south).

3. 11.2 m.p.h. is the established average; the speed varied.

4. Elm Street, also known as "Parkway" because the real Elm Street dead-ends in front of the TSBD.

5. Deep blue; sometimes referred to as midnight blue or"Kennedy blue"; many authors have pictured it as black.

6. The Secret Service follow-up, LBJ's car, and his Secret Service follow-up.

7. 266 feet.

8. No; some vehicles near the end of the parade continued on to the Trade Mart.

9. Stemmons Freeway.

10. 20,000. The estimate is from Secret Service testimony and reports.

SECRET SERVICE—BEGINNER

1. Who was the head of the Secret Service on November 22, 1963?

2. Who was the head of the Dallas Office of the Secret Service?

3. Who was the Secret Service advance agent for the Dallas trip?

4. Who was the Special-Agent-in-Charge for the Dallas trip?

5. Who drove the Presidential limousine during the fatal motorcade?

6. Who was the only agent to come to the President's rescue?

7. With reference to question 6, what was that agent's usual duty?

8. What agent claimed to shield Vice-President Johnson with his body?

9. What agent brandished the AR-15 automatic rifle and was subsequently accused of firing the fatal shot?

10. Who was the head of the White House detail?

Answers on next page

ANSWERS
SECRET SERVICE—BEGINNER

1. James Rowley.

2. Forrest V. Sorrels.

3. Winston Lawson.

4. Roy Kellerman.

5. William Greer.

6. Clint Hill.

7. Protection of Mrs. Kennedy. Hill was a last-minute addition to the trip, as Mrs. Kennedy did not usually go with JFK on political trips.

8. Rufus Youngblood.

9. George Hickey.

10. Gerald Behn.

SECRET SERVICE—EXPERT

1. Who was the head of the Secret Service at the beginning of JFK's term?

2. Name as many as possible of the eight agents in the follow-up car.

3. What was the code designation for the follow-up car?

4. What was the code designation for the Presidential car?

5. What Secret Service agent is pictured in the swearing-in of President Johnson?

6. What lapel pins were worn by the Secret Service to distinguish them from non-agents?

7. What establishment did the Secret Service frequent on the night of November 21-22?

8. Who, besides the agents, were in the follow-up car?

9. What Secret Service agent handled the magic bullet?

10. What Secret Service agent drove the "President's car" in the Warren Commission's re-creation of the event?

Answers on next page

ANSWERS
SECRET SERVICE—EXPERT

1. U.E. Baughman. He would later endorse Warren Commissioner Dulles's theory that assassins are "lone nuts."

2. Landis, Ready, Hill, and McIntryre on the running boards; Bennett and Hickey, perched on the rear seats, and Roberts and Kinney, the driver, in the front seats.

3. SS 679.

4. SS 100 X.

5. Lem Johns, to the right of and well behind LBJ, as you look at the traditional swearing-in photo.

6. White with a red bar. They were standard; not a unique emblem as suggested in the movie *Executive Action*.

7. The Cellar.

8. Presidential Assistants Dave Powers and Ken O'Donnell. The oddity here is the question "Why?" They were not in any protective capacity, and it is nonsense to think that JFK would have yelled back to them for policy considerations during a motorcade.

9. Richard Johnsen. (A recent researcher, Vince Palamara, has interviewed Johnsen, and the latter does not seem to have a clear recollection of having the bullet.)

10. George Hickey. It was not, however, the 1961 Lincoln, but rather the 1956 Cadillac, so the exactitude of the survey is skewed by the differing specifications of the two automobiles.

EYEWITNESSES—BEGINNER

1. Name the steamfitter who claimed to have seen a man with a rifle on the sixth floor of the Depository, but was unable to identify anyone in a police lineup.

2. Name the 15-year-old who testified that he saw a weapon in the window, but could not tell if the person was a Caucasian or an African-American.

3. Name the married high-school student who claimed to have seen a weapon at the other end of the TSBD at least fifteen minutes before the arrival of the motorcade.

4. Name the eyewitness who saw the shooting from the lawn, and thought that the Kennedys had a dog in the car; this person would also name the picket fence area "the knoll."

5. What officer encountered Oswald within 90 seconds of the shooting?

6. Whom was that officer with?

7. What reporter in Dealey Plaza wrote a story saying the bullets came from the direction of the knoll, only to have the story pulled in later editions?

8. Name the hysterical waitress who claimed to have witnessed the shooting of Officer Tippit.

9. Name the witness, standing on the Triple Underpass, who told the Commission that at least one shot was fired from under the trees on the knoll.

10. Name the witness in the railroad tower behind the Depository.

Answers on next page

ANSWERS
EYEWITNESSES—BEGINNER

1. Howard Brennan.

2. Amos Lee Euins.

3. Arnold Rowlands.

4. Jean Hill.

5. Marrion L. Baker.

6. TSBD manager Roy Truly.

7. Mary Woodward.

8. Helen Markham.

9. S. M. Holland.

10. Lee Bowers.

EYEWITNESSES—EXPERT

1. Name the eyewitness, in the doorway of the Depository, who resembled Oswald and testified that the shots came from down toward the Triple Underpass.

2. Name the eyewitness who was perched on the Terminal Annex Building, then under construction.

3. Name the bus-driver and cabbie who transported Oswald following the shooting.

4. Name the cabbie who witnessed the Tippit shooting.

5. Name the two car salesmen who witnessed Oswald leaving the scene of the Tippit shooting.

6. Name the husband and wife pictured in many photos at the time protecting their two children; they claimed the shots came from "the garden behind them."

7. Name the man who was on television, emotionally, on November 22, to discuss what he had seen; he would later appear in the Spence-Bugliosi "Oswald trial."

8. Name the three Depository workers directly beneath the "sniper's window."

9. Name the sheriff's officer who believed he saw Oswald run from the Depository and enter a Rambler station wagon to effect his escape.

10. Name any eyewitness that identified Oswald in a police lineup as the person on the sixth floor of the Depository with the gun.

Answers on next page

ANSWERS
EYEWITNESSES—EXPERT

1. Billy N. Lovelady.

2. J.C. Price. Another witness named Richard Carr was in a similar high perch with a commanding view.

3. Cecil McWatters drove the bus; William Whaley drove the cab.

4. William Scoggins.

5. Warren Reynolds and Ted Callaway.

6. William and Gayle Newman.

7. Charles Brehm.

8. Harold Norman, Bonnie Ray Williams, and James "Junior" Jarman.

9. Roger Craig.

10. No one ever made such an identification.

THE ZAPRUDER FILM—BEGINNER

1. What was Mr. Zapruder's first name?

2. Was the Zapruder film in color or black and white?

3. What millimeter film was the Zapruder film?

4. What magazine bought and subsequently published still-frames from the movie?

5. How many frames per second were exposed by Zapruder's camera?

6. Where was Zapruder standing during the filming?

7. What was Abraham Zapruder's occupation?

8. What obstruction weakens the overall effect of the film?

9. When was the Zapruder film first shown on television?

10. How much was Zapruder paid for the film?

Answers on next page

ANSWERS
ZAPRUDER FILM—BEGINNER

1. Abraham.

2. Color.

3. 8mm.

4. *Life*.

5. 18.3 frames per second.

6. Zapruder was standing atop a concrete abutment at the end of the cement arcade west of the Book Depository.

7. Dressmaker.

8. A sign blocks the view of Kennedy for a critical time period.

9. 1975.

10. $150,000.

THE ZAPRUDER FILM—INTERMEDIATE

1. In what frame does Kennedy emerge from behind the road sign?

2. What frames are missing from the film as published by the Warren Commission?

3. Why are those frames missing?

4. In what frame does the President's head seem to explode?

5. What did Zapruder repeat several times after the filming?

6. Who accompanied Zapruder to take the film?

7. What ultimately caused Zapruder to take the film?

8. What kind of movie camera was Zapruder using?

9. How old was the camera?

10. What was unique about Mr. Zapruder's testimony before the Warren Commission?

Answers on next page

ANSWERS: THE ZAPRUDER FILM—INTERMEDIATE

1. His left arm becomes visible in Frame 223.

2. Frames 208-211.

3. It has been claimed that they were damaged in processing.

4. Frame 313.

5. "They've killed him,...they've killed him."

6. Marilyn Sitzman, Zapruder's secretary.

7. The weather improved rapidly on the morning of the 22nd.

8. Bell and Howell.

9. It was new.

10. Zapruder wept through much of his testimony.

ZAPRUDER FILM—EXPERT

1. How long does the entire Zapruder film run?

2. How many "frames" are there?

3. In what frame is there the strongest suggestion of an outline of a gunman in the foliage near the picket fence?

4. Who owns the Zapruder film?

5. What photo-optic researcher has done the best work in enhancing the Zapruder film?

6. What researcher has subjected the film to infra-red technology to actually "show" the bullets passing through the frames?

7. Name two "suspects" shown in the film.

8. Where did Zapruder believe the shots came from?

9. Who is the little girl seen running along with JFK's car, then turning sharply and looking back?

10. How did Zapruder's testimony before the Warren Commission end?

Answers on next page

ANSWERS
THE ZAPRUDER FILM—EXPERT

1. 26.55 seconds.

2. 486 frames.

3. Frame 413.

4. It was deeded back to the Zapruder family by Time-Life.

5. Robert Groden.

6. Robert Morningstar.

7. "The Umbrella Man" and "The man in black" (in addition to the "suspect" suggested in question number 3). The movie also shows both Secret Service agents who have been listed as suspects.

8. Behind him.

9. Rosemary Willis, daughter of Phil Willis.

10. Mr. Zapruder said that he had heard there was more than one person involved in the assassination; he was told in reply that his film had been very helpful.

PHOTO EVIDENCE—INTERMEDIATE

1. A friend of Jean Hill's took several polaroid photos, at least two of which were confiscated. Name this person who did not appear before the Warren Commission.

2. Close behind Jean Hill and her friend was a lady with headgear on who also had photographs seized. Name her and give her "nickname."

3. A soldier on leave took films from the Grassy Knoll, and they too were confiscated. Name him.

4. Two films were taken almost exactly opposite from Zapruder's position at the time of the shooting. Name the man who took a film that his grandchildren are still trying to recover the original print of.

5. Name the lady who took a similar film.

6. Name the Associated Press photographer who was chased off the Triple Underpass and later took a photo showing an Oswald look-alike in the TSBD doorway.

7. Name the man who took a movie showing two figures on the sixth floor of the TSBD seconds before the shooting.

8. Name the man who took a similar film of the TSBD.

9. Name the WW II veteran who took a series of slides, one virtually at the second of the first shot.

10. Name the FBI agent who "shot" the films of the re-creation of the assassination.

Answers on next page

ANSWERS
PHOTO EVIDENCE—INTERMEDIATE

1. Mary Moorman. She has since changed her name for the sake of relative anonymity.

2. Beverly Oliver, the "Babushka lady".

3. Gordon Arnold.

4. Orville Nix.

5. Mary Muchmore.

6. James Altgens.

7. C. L. Bronson.

8. Robert Hughes.

9. Phil Willis.

10. Lyndal Shaneyfelt.

PARKLAND HOSPITAL—INTERMEDIATE

1. Who were the two senior physicians in attendance in the efforts to revive President Kennedy?

2. Five surgical incisions, in addition to the tracheostomy, were made on the President; name or describe them.

3. Name the nurse, recently arrived in America, who treated the President.

4. Who was the first doctor to examine the President?

5. Name two doctors who attended Governor Connally.

6. Name one nurse who attended the governor.

7. Which Secret Service Agent was present in the emergency room with his gun out in case of trouble?

8. Which doctor published a book about his experiences in the emergency room?

9. What priest is credited with having given the last rites to the President?

10. Who was the orderly who cleaned the President's body so it could be placed in an expensive coffin?

Answers on next page

ANSWERS
PARKLAND HOSPITAL—INTERMEDIATE

1. Dr. William Kemp Clark and Dr. Malcolm Perry.

2. They were referred to as cutdowns; two were made in the upper chest for possible drainage; one was made in each leg and one arm to infuse the President with blood and other fluids that related to shock or his Addison's condition.

3. Diana Bowron. She continued her penchant for travel after the events of November 22, and was quite difficult to locate by researchers seeking additional data. When she was found, her story and facts seem exaggerated.

4. Dr. Midgett; he helped wheel the President in; otherwise, his name is lost to posterity.

5. Dr. Shires, Dr. Gregory, Dr. Duke, Dr. Crenshaw.

6. Jeanette Standridge, Jane Wester, Henrietta Ross.

7. Clint Hill.

8. Dr. Charles Crenshaw (*Conspiracy of Silence*).

9. Father Oscar Huber. He had watched the motorcade from a vantage point after Dealey Plaza, so he did not get to see President Kennedy. He was quickly summoned to view JFK in a manner he did not expect.

10. David Sanders. Although hardly qualified in the medical sense, he had an outstanding view of JFK's wounds. He was not called by the WC.

PARKLAND HOSPITAL—EXPERT

1. What was JFK's admitting number to Parkland?

2. How many numbers later in sequence was Texas Governor John Connally?

3. What did Mrs. Kennedy kiss upon learning of her husband's death?

4. In which room was the President treated?

5. Which Secret Service agent removed his coat and placed it over the upper extremities of the President?

6. What was the President's blood type?

7. What type of blood is safe to give any patient?

8. Who pronounced the President dead?

9. What item of the President's was left behind and caused some concern for the Parkland staff?

10. What, according to Senator Mike Mansfield's eulogy, did Mrs. Kennedy do after kissing her late husband?

Answers on next page

ANSWERS
PARKLAND HOSPITAL—EXPERT

1. 24740

2. 3; 24743.

3. JFK's big toe.

4. Trauma Room 1.

5. Clint Hill.

6. O positive.

7. O negative.

8. Dr. William Kemp Clark.

9. JFK's wrist watch. (Of note: This event is referenced in many contemporary Parkland in-house reports; none of those reports contains any reference in any place to the "magic bullet" supposedly found at Parkland. Food for thought.)

10. She took off her wedding ring and put it on one of JFK's fingers.

BETHESDA—BEGINNER

1. Name the three autopsists who performed the pathological examination on the President.

2. Which of the three autopsy doctors was not in the Navy?

3. With respect to the answer to question 2, what other prominent autopsy did that doctor take part in?

4. What time did the motorcade from Andrews Air Force Base arrive at Bethesda?

5. On what floor did the Kennedy entourage stay during the autopsy procedure?

6. Who was the President's personal physician, who would later verify the Bethesda autopsy face-sheets?

7. What law-enforcement officer took custody of all photographs taken at Bethesda?

8. What major piece of "evidence" pertaining to the autopsy would later be listed as "missing"?

9. In what color ambulance did Kennedy's body arrive (according to the "official version")?

10. How many autopsies can be performed at any given time in the Bethesda morgue that existed in 1963?

Answers on next page

ANSWERS
BETHESDA—BEGINNER

1. James J. Humes, J. Thornton Boswell, and Pierre Finck.

2. Lt. Col. Finck was in the U.S. Army.

3. Robert F. Kennedy in June 1968.

4. 7:00 pm, EST.

5. The seventeenth floor.

6. Admiral George W. Burkley. The only doctor to be present at both Bethesda and Parkland, and the doctor who "verified" the autopsy face-sheets, he was not called by the WC.

7. Secret Service Agent Roy Kellerman.

8. JFK's brain.

9. Gray.

10. There were two lab tables in the 1963 Bethesda Morgue. It has been totally remade since 1963.

BETHESDA—EXPERT

1. Who was the radiologist at Bethesda for John Kennedy's autopsy?

2. Who were the two X-ray technicians assisting the person in question 1?

3. Who were the two technicians assisting the pathologists during the autopsy?

4. A lawsuit was filed in 1993 for release of all the photos and X-rays taken of President Kennedy. What was the suggested number of these exposures in the suit?

5. Who took the photos of President Kennedy at the autopsy?

6. Name three Naval officers present at the autopsy who outranked any of the pathologists.

7. Name the person who took "crowd shots" of the autopsy, only to have his film seized and exposed to light.

8. What was curious about the wording of the first two paragraphs of the clinical summary of JFK's autopsy?

9. How much did Kennedy's brain weigh, according to autopsy documents?

10. When did the autopsy doctors first view the President's clothing?

Answers on next page

ANSWERS
BETHESDA—EXPERT

1. Dr. John Ebersole.

2. Jerrol Custer and Edward Reed.

3. James Curtis Jenkins and Paul O'Connor.

4. 257.

5. John Stringer and Floyd Riebe.

6. Calvin Galloway, Robert Canada, and John Stover.

7. William Bruce Pitzer, who would later die under mysterious circumstances, which were officially ruled suicide.

8. They explained where the car was with relationship to the rifle that had been seen by witnesses, which virtually foretold the remaining autopsy findings.

9. 1500 grams.

10. The day before their Warren Commission testimony in March 1964.

MEDIA—INTERMEDIATE

1. Which was the first major network to interrupt programming on
   November 22?

2. What program did they interrupt?

3. What news did they have about Kennedy?

4. What anchorman came close to weeping when he announced the death
   of John Kennedy?

5. What future anchorman was present, just west of Dealey Plaza, and would
   file numerous reports on the assassination?

6. What highly respected journalist reported seeing Jack Ruby at Parkland
   Hospital shortly after the President was pronounced dead?

7. What two journalists interviewed Oswald in the early phase of
   his "defection"?

8. Who was the New Orleans radio personality who arranged for Oswald
   to debate two anti-Castro people.

9. Whom did Oswald debate?

10. In the movie *JFK*, Garrison's investigation is ridiculed in a news special.
    How many people did Garrison/Costner estimate were watching this
    media assault?

Answers on next page

ANSWERS
MEDIA—INTERMEDIATE

1. CBS.

2. *As the World Turns*.

3. JFK was known to have been shot and seriously wounded.

4. Walter Cronkite.

5. Dan Rather.

6. Seth Kantor.

7. Priscilla Johnson and Aline Mosby.

8. Bill Stuckey.

9. Dr. Carlos Bringuier and Ed Butler.

10. Twenty to thirty million.

OTHER SUSPECTS—EXPERT

1. What well-known figure in the Kennedy case was taken into custody, had a weapon seized at his residence, and was requested to take a polygraph exam?

2. What individual with multiple arrests was detained, only to sign himself out of custody using the name "Jim Braden."

3. In what building was "Braden" arrested?

4. Who was the individual of suspicious background and suspicious behavior on November 22 who was employed by a Lincoln-Mercury dealership?

5. What police officer was named by his widow and son as a shooter in the Dealey Plaza crossfire?

6. What other Dallas officer was believed to have been in a position overlooking Dealey Plaza with a high-powered rifle?

7. What suspect was taken into custody by Jim Leavelle?

8. What suspect was tracked and arrested in Fort Worth?

9. What person, accused of subversive activities, had his home raided at 1:30 AM by police and was soon fired from the Depository?

10. Name the three tramps — as their names exist on the Dallas records.

Answers on next page

ANSWERS
OTHER SUSPECTS—EXPERT

1. Wesley Frazier, who had driven Oswald to work on November 22.

2. Eugene Hale Brading.

3. The Dal-Tex Building.

4. Jack Lawrence.

5. Roscoe White.

6. Harry Weatherford.

7. Donald Sharpe.

8. Donald Wayne House.

9. Joe R. Molina. He had been a long-time TSBD employee, yet his employment was terminated shortly after the assassination on the pretext that the TSBD was becoming more automated.

10. Gus Abrams, John Forrester Gedney, and Harold Doyle were the names recorded for posterity.

CIA—INTERMEDIATE

1. In what year was the CIA created?

2. What had performed the function earlier?

3. What public official showed great desire to head the CIA?

4. What Eisenhower military aide headed the CIA?

5. Who was Director of the CIA during the Eisenhower years?

6. Who was his Deputy?

7. Which CIA operation did Oswald definitely have a connection to?

8. Who assisted the Director and Deputy Director plan for the Bay of Pigs, and was dismissed with them?

9. Who did JFK appoint to head the CIA?

10. Who was his deputy?

Answers on next page

ANSWERS
CIA—INTERMEDIATE

1. 1947.

2. O.S.S. (Office of Strategic Services).

3. J. E. Hoover.

4. Walter Bedell Smith.

5. Allan Dulles.

6. General Charles Cabell.

7. The U-2.

8. Richard Bissell.

9. John McCone.

10. Richard Helms.

OSWALD IN THE MARINES—INTERMEDIATE

1. At what age did Oswald first try to join the Marine Corps?

2. At what age did Oswald eventually join the Marine Corps?

3. What well-known movie star was captured accidently in a photograph with Marine Oswald in the background?

4. How many times was Oswald court-martialed, and for what?

5. Where was Oswald's most famous overseas posting?

6. What did the phrase "in the bubble" mean to Oswald while in the Marines?

7. What did the phrase "90 angels" mean?

8. Where was Oswald's last posting?

9. When was Oswald discharged and under what circumstances?

10. When was Oswald's discharge changed, and under what circumstances?

Answers on next page

ANSWERS
OSWALD IN THE MARINES—INTERMEDIATE

1. 16.

2. 17. Six days after his seventeenth birthday.

3. John Wayne.

4. Twice; Once for having a private weapon, and the second time for pouring a drink over a sergeant.

5. Atsugi in Japan, where the U-2 was located.

6. Operating a radar screen in a darkened atmosphere.

7. 90,000 feet of altitude — top flying altitude for the U-2.

8. El Toro Air Station, Santa Ana, California.

9. September 11, 1959 — supposedly because of an injury to his mother.

10. Late summer, 1960, as Oswald was unable to attend reserve meetings because he was living in Minsk, USSR. He was thus given a "less than honorable discharge" from the Marine Reserves, not the traditional "dishonorable discharge" from the Marines.

OSWALD IN USSR—INTERMEDIATE

1. From what U.S. city did Oswald leave to reach the Soviet Union?

2. From which country did Oswald enter the USSR?

3. Oswald admitted to being questioned by what Soviet agency?

4. Name the two journalists who interviewed Oswald early in his stay in Moscow.

5. Name the two American consulate officers who witnessed Oswald's attempt to "renounce his citizenship."

6. At the time of his renunciation effort, where did Oswald claim his Soviet citizenship was being considered?

7. Give the first name of the Intourist guide for whom Oswald left the suicide note when he thought he was being expelled from the USSR.

8. To what city was Oswald sent when he was allowed to remain in the USSR?

9. What was Oswald's primary occupation (besides suspected spy) in the USSR?

10. What Soviet defector would later claim to have full knowledge of Oswald's activities in the Soviet Union?

Answers on next page

ANSWERS
OSWALD IN USSR—INTERMEDIATE

1. New Orleans.

2. Finland.

3. The M.V.D., an "internal security organ" vaguely analogous to our FBI.

4. Priscilla Johnson and Aline Mosby.

5. Richard Snyder and John McVickar.

6. By the Supreme Soviet.

7. Rima.

8. Minsk.

9. Oswald worked in a plant where radios were made.

10. Yuri Nosenko.

OSWALD'S RETURN TO AMERICA—INTERMEDIATE

1. Approximately how long did it take for Oswald's request to return to the U.S. take to be processed?

2. What was the biggest obstacle(s) to overcome in order to return to the United States?

3. How much was Oswald loaned to return to the United States?

4. Who made the loan?

5. Was the loan ever repaid?

6. How did the Oswalds reach Holland?

7. How did the Oswalds reach the United States?

8. Who greeted the Oswalds upon their entry into the United States?

9. How did the Oswalds reach Texas?

10. What was Oswald's biggest disappointment, as related to his return?

Answers on next page

ANSWERS
OSWALD'S RETURN TO AMERICA—INTERMEDIATE

1. Ten months to a year.

2. Oswald had married a Soviet national; the birth of a child would be
   a slight additional complication.

3. $435.71.

4. The State Department.

5. Oswald repaid every penny.

6. By train.

7. By boat.

8. Spas T. Raikin, a highly placed member of the Traveler's Aid Society,
   viewed by many as an intelligence front during the peak of the Cold War.

9. By plane.

10. Lack of journalistic coverage of his return.

THE OSWALD FAMILY—BEGINNER

1. Name Oswald's mother.

2. Give Oswald's father's name.

3. When did Oswald's parents die?

4. What was the name of Oswald's half-brother from a previous marriage involving his mother?

5. What was the name of Oswald's brother?

6. What were the names of Oswald's two daughters?

7. Name the man identified as "Oswald's surrogate father."

8. Whom did Oswald's mother marry during Lee's childhood, which allowed him to travel for a brief time?

9. What caused the dissolution of that marriage?

10. What problem with his mother caused Oswald to apply for a hardship discharge from the Marines?

Answers on next page

ANSWER
THE OSWALD FAMILY—BEGINNER

1. Marguerite.

2. Robert E. Lee Oswald.

3. Oswald's father died before Lee was born, in August of 1939, of a coronary attack while mowing the lawn. Mrs. Oswald died in 1981.

4. John Pic.

5. Robert Oswald.

6. June and Rachel.

7. Charles "Dutz" Murret. (The surrogate father designation is vastly overstated; Dutz's role in Oswald's life was hardly more than an older, related male.)

8. Edward Ekdahl.

9. Mr. Ekdahl was caught by Marguerite and the boys in an act of infidelity.

10. A jar fell on her in January 1959; she was fully recovered by the time Oswald applied for his hardship discharge.

THE OSWALD FAMILY—EXPERT

1. What was Lee Oswald's mother's maiden name?

2. Name Mrs. Oswald's three husbands.

3. Oswald expected his wife's first pregnancy to result in the birth of a son; what name had Oswald chosen for the boy?

4. What was Marina's maiden name?

5. What is Marina's last name today?

6. Which family member was prohibited by the Secret Service from attending Oswald's funeral?

7. Where is Lee Oswald buried?

8. How were Oswald's brother and half-brother employed at the time of the assassination?

9. How long before the assassination had Oswald last seen his mother?

10. To which relative did Oswald come in close proximity while in Japan?

Answers on next page

ANSWERS
THE OSWALD FAMILY—EXPERT

1. Claviere.

2. Edward Pic, Robert Oswald, Edward Ekdahl.

3. David Lee Oswald. Lee Oswald listed this name on a document prepared in the USSR before Marina gave birth to a girl.

4. Prussakova; there are alternate spellings.

5. Porter.

6. Half-brother John Pic.

7. Rose Hill Cemetery, Fort Worth, Texas. Marguerite Oswald, continuing her "my son was an agent" story, gave consideration to having Oswald re-interred at Arlington.

8. Robert worked for a brick company, and John Pic was a career service man in the Coast Guard.

9. The previous Thanksgiving.

10. Cousin Marilyn Murret.

MARINA OSWALD—BEGINNER

1. Where was Marina born?

2. In what occupation was she trained?

3. When did she meet Lee Oswald?

4. Where did she meet Lee Oswald?

5. Where did Lee and Marina have several subsequent meetings?

6. When did Lee and Marina marry?

7. With whom was Marina residing at the time of her courtship with Lee Oswald?

8. With whom did Marina live in the U.S. during her second pregnancy?

9. What was Marina's biggest health concern during the eighteen months she lived with Lee Oswald in the United States?

10. Where does Marina reside today?

Answers on next page

ANSWERS
MARINA OSWALD—BEGINNER

1. Archangel.

2. Pharmacist.

3. March 1961.

4. At a trade-union dance.

5. In a hospital; Oswald was having problems with his adenoids.

6. April 30, 1961.

7. Her uncle, an officer in the M.V.D. (internal security).

8. Ruth Paine.

9. Her teeth.

10. In an extremely beautiful country setting not all that far outside
    of Dallas.

MARINA OSWALD—EXPERT

1. What was Marina Oswald's patronym (name given from father)?

2. When (month and year) was she born?

3. How many "backyard photos" did Marina admit to taking?

4. What American political figure did Marina claim Oswald was going to shoot before she prevented him from leaving by locking him in the bathroom?

5. Who took Marina away from Lee when there were concerns about Lee being a wife-beater?

6. Who translated Marina's responses at police headquarters on November 22, 1963?

7. Who became Marina's attorney and manager during her Secret Service confinement?

8. What is the most commonly suggested dollar figure for donations received by Marina after the assassination?

9. With whom did Marina live after her release from Secret Service protection?

10. Why was Marina requestioned by the Warren Commission on September 6, 1964?

Answers on next page

ANSWERS
MARINA OSWALD—EXPERT

1. Nikolaevna.

2. July 17, 1941.

3. Two.

4. Richard Nixon.

5. Mr. and Mrs. George DeMohrenschildt.

6. Ilya Mamantov.

7. Jim Martin.

8. $57,000.

9. The Martin family, and later the Ray family.

10. There were doubts about the Mexico trip, and Marina had found bus
    stubs in a one-year old Mexican TV guide.

LYNDON B. JOHNSON—INTERMEDIATE

1. What major event in LBJ's life occured in 1955?

2. What claim did LBJ make about JFK at the 1960 convention?

3. Which of JFK's important advisors strongly opposed LBJ on the ticket?

4. What was Johnson's job on the ticket?

5. What else did LBJ run for in 1960?

6. What was unique about the election of JFK and LBJ?

7. What was Johnson's nickname after a close (and suspicious) election in the 1940s?

8. What was Johnson's title in 1960?

9. What three people would get LBJ in trouble between 1961 and 1964?

10. Why did LBJ take the number two spot in 1960?

Answers on next page

ANSWERS
LYNDON B. JOHNSON—INTERMEDIATE

1. A massive heart attack.

2. LBJ claimed that JFK should not be nominated, as Kennedy was then suffering from a fatal disease. (The concept was first floated through LBJ's campaign manager, John Connally.)

3. Robert Kennedy.

4. To carry as much of the South as possible.

5. The Senate; he got special legislation passed in Texas allowing him to do this, in case the JFK-LBJ ticket lost, he would still remain powerful.

6. It was the first time both members of the ticket were Senators; the only other Senators elected in this century were Harding and Truman.

7. "Landslide Lyndon."

8. Senate Majority Leader.

9. Billy Sol Estes, Bobby Baker, and Walter Jenkins.

10. He told an interviewer that one out of four Presidents died in office, and he, LBJ, was a gamblin' man.

LYNDON JOHNSON, NOVEMBER 22—INTERMEDIATE

1. To whom did LBJ introduce JFK on the morning of November 22?

2. What two statements did JFK make involving LBJ on November 22?

3. What plane did LBJ occupy on the way to Dallas?

4. Whose plane landed first?

5. What other politician was in Johnson's car?

6. Who drove Johnson's car?

7. Where did LBJ stay in Parkland Hospital?

8. Who drove LBJ back to the Airport?

9. Who swore in LBJ?

10. Where did LBJ go after Air Force One returned to Washington?

Answers on next page

ANSWERS
LYNDON JOHNSON, NOVEMBER 22—INTERMEDIATE

1. LBJ introduced JFK to LBJ's sister.

2. He supposedly said that the Democrats would carry Texas and Massachusetts; he is also alleged to have claimed that LBJ would be dumped from the 1964 ticket.

3. *Air Force Two*.

4. Johnson's plane landed first, so he would be part of the welcoming committee for JFK.

5. Senator Ralph Yarborough.

6. State trooper Hurchel Jacks.

7. In a "Minor Medicine" area.

8. Jesse Curry. (Thus at no time in Texas was LBJ driven by Secret Service.)

9. Judge Sarah T. Hughes.

10. Right to the White House.

J. EDGAR HOOVER—INTERMEDIATE

1. In what year did Hoover become the Director of the FBI?

2. On November 22, who was Hoover's nominal boss?

3. How did Hoover learn of JFK's death?

4. John Kennedy had one armoured limousine on November 22; how many did Hoover have on that day?

5. What does the "J" stand for in "J. Edgar"?

6. Who was the number-two man in the FBI on November 22?

7. What was Hoover's favorite form of gambling?

8. Where did Hoover spend Saturday, November 23, 1963?

9. What prominent American politician had been Hoover's neighbor for 19 years?

10. How many times did Hoover vote for Presidential candidates?

Answers on next page

ANSWERS
J. EDGAR HOOVER—INTERMEDIATE

1. 1924.

2. Attorney General Robert F. Kennedy.

3. Hoover called RFK at home and told him that JFK had been shot and hung up abruptly. Hoover called RFK a second time, to tell him the President was in critical condition; RFK told him, "My brother is dead."

4. Four.

5. John.

6. Clyde Tolson.

7. Horse racing.

8. At the race track.

9. Lyndon Johnson.

10. None. Until Kennedy's term, Washington residents had no Presidential electors. By then, Hoover did not have to vote for the President; he usually owned him.

J. EDGAR HOOVER—EXPERT

1. When was Hoover born?

2. Based on his birth date, when would Hoover have had to retire by statute in the absence of Presidential exemption?

3. What happened to Hoover's father?

4. Hoover lived with his mother until what age?

5. What future President was once denied admission to the FBI?

6. What agent was so successful in bringing gangsters to justice that Hoover became jealous of him and eventually forced him into a life that culminated in suicide?

7. How did Hoover describe Oswald before the Warren Commission?

8. Who was Hoover's private secretary for most of his career?

9. With whom did Hoover side in a major political battle before becoming Director, a move that almost cost him his career?

10. What was Hoover's reported response when Clyde Tolson asked to be buried alongside him?

Answers on next page

ANSWER
J. EDGAR HOOVER—EXPERT

1. January 1, 1895.

2. January 1, 1965, his seventieth birthday.

3. He was confined to a mental institution for chronic depression and ultimately lost the will to live and died.

4. Hoover lived with his mother until he was 43.

5. Richard Nixon had wanted to join the FBI.

6. Melvin Purvis, the symbol of the "G-man" in the 1930s.

7. Oswald was seen by Hoover as "a dedicated Communist."

8. Helen Gandy.

9. In 1919-20, Hoover took the side of then Attorney General A. Mitchell Palmer, who launched a series of "raids" leading to the arrest of several thousand suspected "reds."

10. Hoover told Tolson it was not necessary for Tolson to purchase a grave— Hoover only planned to be in his for three days.

OSWALD'S ARREST—BEGINNER

1. Where was Oswald arrested?

2. At what time was Oswald arrested?

3. Where was Oswald located, in the specific building, at the time of his arrest?

4. What were Oswald's supposed words at the time of his arrest?

5. Who had pointed Oswald out to the police after following him from a shoe store?

6. Who called the police?

7. How many other civilians were present at the time of Oswald's arrest?

8. Which officer did Oswald punch?

9. What did Oswald yell as he was being subdued?

10. Were any law-enforcement officers besides Dallas police present when Oswald was arrested, and if so, who?

Answers on next page

ANSWERS
OSWALD'S ARREST—BEGINNER

1. At the Texas Theater.

2. 1:51 p.m.

3. In the center of the theater, about four rows from the back, slightly to the left of the center of the section.

4. "It's all over now." Others heard "This is it."

5. Shoe salesman Johnny Brewer.

6. Ticket seller Julia Postal.

7. The theater contained an estimated 15-20 patrons.

8. M.N. McDonald.

9. "I am not resisting arrest."

10. Two FBI agents, Robert Barrett and Bardwell Odum, were present in addition to assistant D.A. William Alexander.

OSWALD'S ARREST—EXPERT

1. Prior to converging on the location where Oswald was arrested, where did police initially arrive looking for a suspect?

2. Who is the detective with the cigar shown in pictures of Oswald being put in the squad car?

3. Who was running the theater concession stand and thought that Oswald had arrived when the feature started?

4. What was playing?

5. How much did the ticket, which Oswald did not buy, cost?

6. How many patrons present in the place where Oswald was arrested would later testify before the Warren Commission?

7. What did the FBI conclude with respect to the bullets in Oswald's gun at the time of his arrest?

8. What suspect were the police looking for when they arrested Oswald?

9. On what street is the arrest site located?

10. What parallel to Lincoln's assassination does Oswald's arrest suggest?

Answers on next page

ANSWERS
OSWALD'S ARREST—EXPERT

1. At a local library; someone had been seen entering in haste; it was a youth who hurried there to spread the news.

2. Detective Bentley.

3. W. "Butch" Burroughs. (He was still employed there as of 1995.)

4. *War is Hell* and *Cry of Battle*.

5. Seventy-five cents.

6. One.

7. None gave any indications of hammer marks, contradicting the Dallas police statement that Oswald pulled the trigger on the revolver.

8. They were looking for Officer Tippit's killer.

9. Jefferson Street.

10. Lincoln was killed in a theater and his assailant cornered in a barn,the equivalent of a warehouse; JFK's "killer" shot from a warehouse and was captured in a theater.

OSWALD IN CUSTODY—INTERMEDIATE

1. Who was the primary interrogator of Oswald while he was in the custody of the Dallas police?

2. For how many hours was Oswald interrogated?

3. What was the initial concern over Oswald's identity?

4. Whose presence at the interrogation caused Oswald to lose his temper?

5. What was found on Oswald's person when he was searched at the 4 PM lineup?

6. What is the only known piece of evidence that Oswald was physically confronted with?

7. What was Oswald's answer to the press with regard to his participation in the assassination?

8. Who identified Oswald in the police department as the individual he saw making an escape in a Rambler station wagon?

9. Did Oswald make any phone calls while in custody, and if so, to whom?

10. For how much of the time he was in custody did Oswald have legal counsel?

Answers on next page

ANSWERS
OSWALD IN CUSTODY—INTERMEDIATE

1. Homicide chief Will Fritz.

2. A total of twelve hours.

3. Oswald was carrying materials naming him as Oswald as well as "A.J. Hidell."

4. FBI Agent James Hosty.

5. A bus transfer and five live bullets for the revolver.

6. A "backyard photo" of Oswald with the two weapons.

7. "I'm a patsy." He also stated on more than one occasion that he had not shot anyone.

8. Roger Craig.

9. He attempted, with no success, to reach attorney John Abt. It has also been suggested that he tried to reach an exchange in North Carolina. He did manage to get through to Ruth Paine.

10. Oswald never had counsel during his custody.

OSWALD IN CUSTODY—EXPERT

1. Either by name or occupation, who were in the first lineups with Oswald?

2. What did Detective Leavelle tell Oswald shortly before they walked into Jack Ruby?

3. When was Oswald first finger-printed?

4. When (day and time) was Oswald charged and arraigned in the Tippit slaying?

5. When (day and time) was Oswald charged and arraigned in the killing of the President?

6. How did statements made at the midnight press conference involve the nature of question 5 above?

7. When (day and time) was Oswald charged and arraigned with the attempted murder of Governor Connally?

8. Who arraigned Oswald?

9. What caliber gun was mentioned in the Kennedy and Connally arraignment papers?

10. What did Oswald say with respect to the "station wagon" allegation?

Answers on next page

ANSWERS
OSWALD IN CUSTODY—EXPERT

1. Dallas officers Richard Clark and William Perry, and jailer Don Ables.

2. Leavelle reportedly told Oswald that he hoped nobody was waiting outside to shoot at them, and if they were, Leavelle hoped the person or persons were not as good a shot as Oswald. (Note: Leavelle is then shown with his suit-coat buttoned while escorting Oswald—highly irregular police procedure; you keep your coat open if you need to get to your service revolver.)

3. Friday, November 22, at 9 p.m.

4. Friday, November 22, 7:10 p.m.

5. Oswald was charged in the Kennedy case at 11:26 p.m. on November 22, but was not arraigned until 1:35 a.m. on November 23.

6. Oswald indicated at the press conference that he had not been charged with shooting the President, although unknown to him, he had.

7. Oswald was charged with shooting the Governor at 6:30 a.m. on November 23, but he was never arraigned for that charge. It might strike the reader as odd that Oswald was charged and arraigned in the fatal shootings of a New England President and a local officer, but was never arraigned for the shooting of the Governor of the state where the shots were fired.

8. Magistrate David Johnston.

9. With respect to JFK and Connally, the documents referred to a 6.25mm rifle; Tippit's documents mentioned a pistol.

10. Oswald indicated the station wagon (not a new Rambler) belonged to Mrs. Paine, and that they should leave her out of this, as she had nothing to do with it.

JACK RUBY—BEGINNER

1. Give Ruby's name at birth.

2. Give the location of Ruby's childhood.

3. In what year did Ruby "make the move" to Dallas?

4. Name the nightclub Ruby was operating at the time of the assassination.

5. Name Ruby's roommate at the time of the assassination.

6. Name the animal Ruby was noted for keeping as pets.

7. What was Ruby's middle name?

8. What did Ruby photograph in the early hours of November 23, 1963?

9. Whom did Ruby correct at the famous "midnight press conference" of November 22-23, 1963?

10. What is the only foreign country Ruby is known to have visited?

Answers on next page

ANSWERS
JACK RUBY—BEGINNER

1. Jacob Rubenstein.

2. Chicago.

3. 1947.

4. The Carousel Club.

5. George Senator.

6. Dogs.

7. Leon.

8. A billboard saying "Impeach Earl Warren."

9. District Attorney Henry Wade.

10. Cuba.

JACK RUBY—INTERMEDIATE

1. Name a club operated by Ruby prior to the one he was operating on November 22, 1963.

2. With what real-estate connected person did Ruby have discussions shortly before the assassination?

3. Name the two men who were "integral parts" of Ruby's club at the time of the assassination.

4. Name any of the various emcees that had passed through the club.

5. Who had put up money for Ruby to operate the club he was running at the time of the assassination?

6. What police officer did Ruby encounter after he left the "midnight" press conference?

7. What were Ruby's sisters' names?

8. One of Ruby's sisters also operated a club. Name it.

9. To whom did Ruby send a telegram on November 24, 1963?

10. Where did Ruby die?

Answers on next page

ANSWERS
JACK RUBY—INTERMEDIATE

1. The Vegas Club (later run by his sister); The Silver Spur.

2. Bertha Cheek.

3. Andrew Armstrong and Curtis L. Crafard.

4. Wally Weston and Billy DeMar are the two best known.

5. Ralph Paul, owner of a nearby drive-in restaurant. Ruby also received financing from some of his brothers and sisters.

6. Harry Olsen.

7. Eva Grant, Eileen Kaminsky, Marion Carroll, and Anna Volpert.

8. The Vegas Club.

9. Karen B. Carlin, aka "Little Lynn." She was reported dead in 1964, but allegedly resurfaced in 1993 to state that the Ruby telegram to her was a preconceived scam.

10. Parkland Hospital.

JACK RUBY—EXPERT

1. With what notorious mobster was Ruby linked in his youth?

2. For what "offense" had Ruby been institutionalized in his youth?

3. Name Ruby's three brothers.

4. At the time of the assassination, which dog did Ruby frequently refer to as "his wife"?

5. In which branch of the service had Ruby served?

6. With respect to weapons proficiency in the service, what rating did Ruby achieve?

7. With what 1960s gambling operator was Ruby frequently linked?

8. What building was Ruby allegedly in just prior to the shooting of Lee Oswald?

9. Name any of Ruby's strippers—real names and stage names if you are able.

10. Which "group" did Ruby specifically mention as a concern in his testimony to the Warren Commission?

Answers on next page

ANSWERS
JACK RUBY—EXPERT

1. Al Capone

2. General anti-social behavior, but, like Oswald, truancy was singled out.

3. Sam Ruby, Earl Ruby, and Hyman Rubenstein.

4. Sheba.

5. Army Air Corps.

6. Like Oswald, "sharpshooter."

7. Lewis McWillie.

8. The office of Western Union.

9. Janet Conforto ("Jada"); Karen B. Carlin ("Little Lynn") Nancy Powell ("Tammy True") are the best known.

10. The John Birch Society.

OSWALD'S MURDER—INTERMEDIATE

1. At what time, according to best estimates, was Oswald shot?

2. What police officials were on the left and right of Oswald?

3. What police official had preceded Oswald by about ten feet?

4. What reason did Ruby cite for shooting Oswald?

5. What is the best estimate as to the number of policemen present at the time of the shooting?

6. What was Chief Jesse Curry doing at the time of the shooting?

7. Is there any evidence that any police officer suggested to Ruby that Oswald should be killed?

8. What were Ruby's first two statements when placed in custody?

9. How long did Ruby's trial last?

10. Who was the attorney of record?

Answers on next page

ANSWERS
OSWALD'S MURDER—INTERMEDIATE

1. 11:21 a.m., CST, on November 24, 1963.

2. Detective Jim Leavelle was to Oswald's right, and Detective L.C. Graves was to Oswald's left (closest to Ruby).

3. Sixty-eight-year-old Homicide Chief Will Fritz.

4. He claimed he wanted to spare Mrs. Kennedy and her children the ordeal of the trial of Oswald.

5. Sixty to seventy.

6. Talking on the telephone to Dallas Mayor Cabell.

7. In their meeting in the early hours of November 23, Officer Harry Olsen had suggested to Ruby that Oswald should be cut into little pieces.

8. Ruby was quoted as saying, "You all know me, I'm Jack Ruby," and "I planned to shoot the *S.O.B.* three times."

9. Jury selection was fourteen days; the trial lasted ten.

10. Melvin Belli.

OSWALD'S MURDER—EXPERT

1. Who was the officer on duty at the Main Street ramp that Ruby supposedly snuck past?

2. What type of revolver did Ruby use to shoot Oswald?

3. What became of that gun after 1963?

4. What officer drove the police car up the Main Street ramp at the time Ruby was supposedly coming down it?

5. What reporter is seen reaching out to get a statement from Oswald just as Ruby is lunging forward?

6. What reporter is heard saying, "He's been shot…Oswald has been shot"?

7. What judge heard Ruby's case?

8. Cite a major reason for the verdict being overturned.

9. What officer was driving the car that Oswald was to have gotten into?

10. What was to be used as a decoy in the Oswald transfer?

Answers on next page

ANSWERS
OSWALD'S MURDER—EXPERT

1. Roy E. Vaughan.

2. A .38 Colt Cobra.

3. It remained in government custody for many years, and was eventually the subject of a lawsuit to have it returned to the family, which still had not settled Ruby's estate. It was auctioned in 1990-91 for $220K to an anonymous buyer. The buyer foolishly took his prize piece to Washington to show to a friend who worked in the Capitol, where the gun was seized. It was only returned after authorities were convinced it was a piece of history. The owner fired 4,000 rounds with the gun and offered each bullet for sale at $500 (total=two million dollars).

4. Rio Pierce.

5. Ike Pappas.

6. Robert Huffaker.

7. Joe B. Brown.

8. Lack of change of venue; improper jury charge; Brown as presiding judge after he had been present to execute the search warrant on Ruby's dwelling.

9. C. N. Dhority.

10. An armored car, which, as events transpired, was too large to back down the entrance ramp to the basement, so it sat there, visible to all. It would have never been a decent "decoy," as the live TV would have shown Oswald placed in the police car that he never quite reached.

THE WARREN COMMISSION—BEGINNER

1. Who appointed the Commission?

2. When was the Commission established?

3. Name as many of the seven commissioners as possible.

4. Upon which agency did the Commission rely primarily for its data?

5. Where are the Commission's materials stored today?

6. Who is the last surviving member of the Warren Commission?

7. Who was the general counsel to the Commission?

8. Which member wrote a book about his experiences as a member of the Warren Commission?

9. Who published the Warren Commission's *Report* ?

10. How many accompanying volumes of testimony and exhibits were subsequently published?

Answers on next page

ANSWERS
THE WARREN COMMISSION—BEGINNER

1. President Lyndon Johnson.

2. November 29, 1963.

3. Earl Warren, Allan Dulles, Gerald Ford, Richard Russell, Hale Boggs, John Sherman Cooper, and John McCloy.

4. The FBI.

5. The National Archives in Washington, D.C. Because of millions of other non JFK documents at the Archives, some of the materials were moved to a separate location in 1993-1994.

6. Gerald Ford.

7. J. Lee Rankin.

8. Gerald Ford (with John Stiles) *Portrait of the Assassin.* (*Note:* It is recommended fiction.)

9. The Government Printing Office in Washington, D.C.

10. 26. 15 volumes of testimony, comprising 7,909 pages; 11 volumes of exhibits, comprising 9,831 pages; Total=17,740 pages.

THE WARREN COMMISSION—INTERMEDIATE

1. What was the number of the executive order that created the Commission?

2. Name any five of the counsel who took commission depositions.

3. What was the actual name of the "Warren Commission"?

4. Who was the first witness called?

5. Who was the last witness called with members of the Commission present?

6. Who was the last witness deposed by Commission counsel?

7. Where in Washington did the Commission meet?

8. Name two witnesses who gave testimony in the White House.

9. How many witnesses gave testimony with all seven Commissioners present?

10. When will Warren Commission materials that were sequestered finally be released?

Answers on next page

ANSWERS
THE WARREN COMMISSION—INTERMEDIATE

1. Executive order #11130.

2. Francis Adams, Joseph Ball, William T. Coleman, Melvin Eisenberg, Burt Griffin, Leon Hubert, Albert Jenner, Wesley Liebeler, Norman Redlich, W. David Slawson, Arlen Specter, Samuel Stern, and Howard Willens. John Hart Ely, listed as a "staff member" took some testimony also.

3. The President's Commission on the Assassination of President Kennedy.

4. Marina Oswald.

5. Marina Oswald.

6. John E. Gallagher, an FBI agent in the physics and chemistry section who testified about neutron activation analysis.

7. The Veteran's Building, 200 Maryland Avenue, N.E.

8. Kenneth O'Donnell; Dave Powers; Lawrence O'Brien.

9. *None.*

10. 2039 A.D.

WARREN COMMISSION—EXPERT

1. How many witnesses were sworn and gave verbal testimony to either the Commissioners or to Counsel?

2. How many witnesses gave testimony before any of the seven Commissioners?

3. Which witness was asked the most questions?

4. Which witness was asked the fewest questions?

5. Which witness did Counsel Burt Griffin call a "d--- l---"?

6. Name the two people who testified to Jack Ruby's presence at Parkland Hospital on the afternoon of November 22.

7. Which two members of the Commission took testimony from Jack Ruby, and where was the testimony taken?

8. Whose testimony included the phrase, "Reference to wounds deleted"?

9. Which Commissioner attended only six sessions where witnesses gave testimony?

10. How many expert marksmen were able to duplicate Oswald's alleged shooting ability in Warren Commission re-creations of the crime?

Answers on next page

ANSWERS
WARREN COMMISSION—EXPERT

1. 488.

2. 93.

3. Ruth Paine, with 5,236.

4. Robert Carswell, with five; the questions related to Secret Service protection for the Speaker of the House.

5. Dallas reserve officer William Newman.

6. Seth Kantor and Wilma Tice.

7. Earl Warren and Gerald Ford; Dallas County Jail.

8. Mrs. John F. Kennedy. Mrs. Kennedy, in her very brief testimony, volunteered information about JFK's wounds. For reasons as yet unknown, the phrase "reference to wounds deleted" superceded her testimony.

9. Richard Russell.

10. *None.*

WARREN COMMISSION WITNESSES—BEGINNER

1. Which witness gave the only testimony suggesting Oswald's involvement in the Walker shooting?

2. What lawyer gave testimony to the Commission, was refused the right to serve as counsel, and was then flown back to Washington at Commission expense to be asked questions he could not answer?

3. How many "Oswalds" testified before the Commission?

4. How many other relatives testified?

5. What did Oswald's mother insist was the purpose for Oswald's trip to Russia?

6. What was on the cover of *Life* during the testimony of Robert Oswald?

7. What person in JFK's limousine testified he heard the President say, "My God, I am hit"?

8. According to Wesley Frazier, what was the only topic Oswald seemed to enjoy discussing?

9. Whose testimony involved great confusion between Oswald and a teenager who found the assassination less than serious?

10. When Commander Humes testified about the autopsy findings, where were the other pathologists?

Answers on next page

ANSWERS
WARREN COMMISSION WITNESSES—BEGINNER

1. Marina Oswald.

2. Mark Lane.

3. Three. (Four if you include half-brother John Pic.)

4. Five (including Pic and four Murrets).

5. She insisted he was a U.S. agent.

6. Oswald with his guns. An admittedly retouched "backyard" photo.

7. Roy Kellerman.

8. Children.

9. Bus driver Cecil McWatters.

10. They were present in the hearing room.

WARREN COMMISSION WITNESSES—BEGINNER II

1. Who testified that the President would have had an "uneventful recovery" if he had only sustained the first wound?

2. Who indicated over a dozen times in his testimony that he could not tell the whole truth in the location he was currently in?

3. One witness testified in the presence of the Attorney General. Name the witness.

4. Who testified that he had taken Oswald to two politically oriented meetings in the fall of 1963?

5. Whose testimony took up much time with respect to the location of the light switch and a garage light bulb?

6. Who testified that he failed to identify Oswald in a lineup because he feared there might be a conspiracy and he might be at risk?

7. Name the three African-Americans who were underneath the "sniper's window" during the shooting.

8. Who ate the chicken lunch on the sixth floor?

9. What officer testified to confronting Oswald in a second-floor lunchroom within seconds of the shooting?

10. Who testified to talking with Officer Tippit after he had been felled by the bullets?

Answers on next page

ANSWERS
WARREN COMMISSION WITNESSES—BEGINNER II

1. J. Thornton Boswell.

2. Jack Ruby.

3. Jackie Kennedy.

4. Michael Paine, then estranged husband of Ruth Paine.

5. Ruth Paine.

6. Howard Brennan.

7. Harold Norman, Junior Jarman, and Bonnie Ray Williams.

8. Bonnie Ray Williams.

9. Marrion L. Baker.

10. Helen Markham, who was the center of subsequent controversies.

WARREN COMMISSION WITNESSES—BEGINNER III

1. Which two witnesses absolutely insisted that Governor John Connally was struck by the second bullet?

2. Who testified that he ejected one live round from the rifle found on the sixth floor of the depository?

3. What Dallas officer insisted that an Oswald palmprint was found on the unexposed portion of the Mannlicher-Carcano rifle?

4. What FBI agent made two contacts with Marina Oswald at the Paine residence?

5. Who testified that Oswald could not take a shot at the motorcade on Houston Street because trees were blocking the way?

6. Whose testimony was taken in jail?

7. Who was taken through a labyrinth of questions regarding the stretcher on which he found the "magic bullet"?

8. What witness very close to the limousine insisted that four to six shots were fired?

9. What key witness testified about what he observed from the Triple Underpass?

10. What Sheriff's Department Officer testified to seeing Oswald escape in a Rambler station wagon?

Answers on next page

ANSWERS
WARREN COMMISSION WITNESSES—BEGINNER III

1. Governor and Mrs. Connally.

2. Dallas Homicide Chief Will Fritz.

3. Dallas Crime Lab Chief Carl Day.

4. James Hosty.

5. J. Edgar Hoover.

6. Jack Ruby.

7. Parkland Hospital engineer Darrell Tomlinson.

8. Jean Hill.

9. Railroad supervisor S.M. Holland.

10. Sheriff's Deputy Roger Craig.

WARREN COMMISSION WITNESSES—BEGINNER IV

1. Who testified to events as seen from the railroad tower?

2. Who testified to being in the doorway of the TSBD, and bore a striking resemblance to Oswald?

3. Where did the witness in question 2 think the shots came from?

4. Which landlady gave testimony that "Mr. Lee" was always at the roominghouse from five o'clock on?

5. Who provided a tentative identification of Oswald at the Tippit scene, and subsequently, this witness's look-alike brother was shot.

6. Who testified that he followed Oswald to the theater, only to find himself manhandled by police, despite his 6'3" height, and then point out Oswald to the police?

7. Who testified that Jack Ruby could not have entered the Main St. ramp while this witness was driving out of it?

8. Who testified with in-depth knowledge of Oswald's postal dealings?

9. Who testified to being the only Secret Service agent to return to Dealey Plaza?

10. Who testified to taking a Mauser rifle into the Depository two days before the motorcade?

Answers on next page

ANSWERS
WARREN COMMISSION WITNESSES—BEGINNER IV

1. Lee Bowers.

2. Billy Lovelady.

3. The concrete arcade.

4. Earline Roberts.

5. Domingo Benavides.

6. Johnny Brewer.

7. Rio Pierce.

8. Postal Inspector Harry Holmes, later revealed to be an FBI informant.

9. Dallas Special Agent in Charge Forrest Sorrels.

10. Warren Caster, who insisted both the Mauser and a .22 left the same day.

WARREN COMMISSION WITNESSES—BEGINNER V

1. What two JFK White House aides gave testimony?

2. What photographer testified that he was chased off the Triple Underpass, despite displaying a Department of Public Safety ID?

3. Which Dealey Plaza groundskeeper testified before the Commission?

4. Only three of "Oswald's friends" from the Marines testified. Who?

5. A member of the Russian *emigre* community, this witness testified to his world travels, his sympathy for Marina, and his kidding of Oswald about the Walker shooting. It may also be that he did not enjoy giving testimony.

6. The attorney Oswald wanted to represent him indicated that he had never heard of Oswald. Who was he?

7. What car salesman testified that Oswald test-drove a vehicle at high speed?

8. A gunsmith told the Warren Commission he found an "Oswald" repair tag on his workbench the day after the assassination. Who?

9. This attorney told that he was contacted by Clay Bertrand to defend Oswald; he also told the Commission he would find out who really killed JFK.

10. She testified to meeting a "Leon Oswald" in late September; the Commission did not believe her. Who is she?

Answers on next page

ANSWERS
WARREN COMMISSION WITNESSES—BEGINNER V

1. Ken O'Donnell and Lawrence O'Brien. (Dave Powers submitted an affadavit.)

2. James Altgens.

3. Emmett Hudson.

4. Nelson Delgado, Kerry Thornley, and Daniel Powers.

5. George DeMohrenschildt.

6. John Abt, who had supposedly never heard of Oswald, but who had gained legal prominence defending clients charged with violation of the Smith Act, which made it illegal to advocate the overthrow of the U.S. government. By some odd coincidence, Abt was nowhere near a telephone during Oswald's all-too-brief survival in custody.

7. Albert G. Bogard.

8. Dial Ryder.

9. Dean Andrews.

10. Sylvia Odio. Her sister Annie supported her story.

WARREN COMMISSION WITNESSES—BEGINNER VI

1. What former Army General testified that he did not believe Oswald had been part of the Walker shooting?

2. What top Dallas law-enforcement officer was not asked any questions about the Kennedy assassination by the Commission?

3. What officer, given the job of guarding the Main Street ramp, denied that Ruby used the ramp for access?

4. What Ruby employee testified that Ruby sent her money by wire?

5. Ruby's jack-of-all-trades at the Carousel Club testified at length. Who was he?

6. Ruby had allowed a roustabout to help out at the Carousel for a month before the shooting. The Commission asked him many questions about his hasty, hitchhike departure from Dallas. Name him.

7. Ruby's business partner and roommate both testified. Name them.

8. The Mayor of Dallas and the City Manager testified. Name them.

9. How many of Ruby's brothers and sisters testified?

10. How many of Ruby's strippers testified?

Answers on next page

ANSWERS
WARREN COMMISSION WITNESSES—BEGINNER VI

1. General Edwin Walker.

2. Sheriff Bill Decker.

3. Roy Vaughan.

4. Karen Carlin.

5. Andrew Armstrong.

6. Curtis L. Crafard.

7. Ralph Paul and George Senator.

8. Earl Cabell and Elgin Crull.

9. Five.

10. Three.

WARREN COMMISSION WITNESSES—INTERMEDIATE

1. Who was the only witness to give testimony in public session?

2. Which witness expressed the wish that Lee Oswald be reburied in Arlington Cemetery?

3. Whom did Robert Oswald believe was part of a conspiracy along with his brother Lee?

4. What witness was willing to give the Commission hearsay about Marina, because she told him she had lied to the FBI?

5. Who testified that at the end of the shooting sequence, "a flurry of shells" came into the car?

6. Where did Arnold Rowland see a weapon on the sixth floor of the Book Depository?

7. Name the two witnesses who saw Oswald with the paper bag.

8. What angle did the pathologists suggest for the wounds they saw?

9. Who testified to finding the cartridges?

10. Which two people found a sixth floor rifle simultaneously?

Answers on next page

ANSWERS
WARREN COMMISSION WITNESSES—INTERMEDIATE

1. Mark Lane, at his insistence.

2. Marguerite Oswald.

3. Jack Ruby.

4. Attorney James Martin.

5. Roy Kellerman

6. The southwest end.

7. Wesley Frazier and his sister, Linnie Mae Randle.

8. 45 degrees.

9. Luke Mooney.

10. Eugene Boone/ Seymour Weitzman.

WARREN COMMISSION WITNESSES—INTERMEDIATE II

1. Who was the cab driver who identified Oswald with respect to the Tippit slaying?

2. How many doctors from Parkland Hospital gave testimony before any of the Warren *Commissioners*?

3. Who were they?

4. How many of Connally's attending physicians testified at the same time as Connally?

5. Who were they?

6. What was the stated purpose of taking testimony from Dallas Police Chief Jesse Curry?

7. Who was in charge of the photographic re-enactment staged in Dealey Plaza?

8. What witness was the head of the Protective Research Section of the Secret Service?

9. Who tried in vain to wave spectators off the Triple Underpass?

10. Who was the FBI handwriting expert called to testify?

Answers on next page

ANSWERS
WARREN COMMISSION WITNESSES—INTERMEDIATE II

1. William Scoggins.

2. Two.

3. Charles "Jim" Carrico and Malcolm Perry.

4. Two.

5. Drs. Gregory and Shaw.

6. Curry was asked to give testimony about "the arrest and death of Lee Oswald."

7. Lyndal Shaneyfelt.

8. Robert Bouck.

9. Winston Lawson.

10. Alwyn Cole.

WARREN COMMISSION WITNESSES—INTERMEDIATE III

1. Which two CIA officials testified together?

2. Who was in overall charge of "basement security" on the morning that Oswald was shot?

3. How many people testified with respect to Oswald's truancy at age 13?

4. What witness had a first and last name that created a palindrome?

5. Which two diplomats testified about Oswald's attempt to renounce his citizenship?

6. How many Dallas doctors gave testimony before Warren Commission staff lawyers only?

7. Whose testimony is listed as having been taken at the Dallas Post Office, but was in fact taken at Parkland Hospital?

8. Which motorcycle officer to the left of the limousine testified about being hit with blood and other matter?

9. Who was the ranking officer at the TSBD until Captain Fritz and Sheriff Decker arrived?

10. Who found both Oswald's jacket and clipboard?

Answers on next page

ANSWERS
WARREN COMMISSION WITNESSES—INTERMEDIATE III

1. John McCone and Richard Helms.

2. Sgt. Patrick Dean.

3. Three; John Carro, Dr. Renatus Hartogs, and Evelyn Siegel.

4. Revilo Oliver.

5. Richard Snyder and John McVickar.

6. Fifteen.

7. Jean Hill.

8. Bobby Hargis.

9. Inspector Sawyer.

10. Frankie Kaiser.

WARREN COMMISSION WITNESSES—INTERMEDIATE IV

1. What officer marked the "Tippit hulls" at the scene of the crime, only to discover later that they did not bear his mark?

2. What jail clerk appeared in a lineup with Oswald?

3. Which two employees from Klein's Sporting Goods testified regarding Oswald's purchase of the rifle?

4. Who gave testimony with respect to Oswald purchasing the pistol?

5. Who were the two officers who testified about Oswald's Marine record, specifically with respect to shooting ability and illnesses?

6. Who interviewed Oswald but refused to employ him, all as a result of requests from the Russian *emigre* community?

7. Name the grocer who refused to cash a $189 check belonging to "Oswald"?

8. Who testified that "Oswald" shot at the wrong target at a rifle range?

9. Who were the two ladies who identified the Oswald family as having been in a furniture store?

10. Two witnesses had the same name; who were they?

Answers on next page

ANSWERS
WARREN COMMISSION WITNESSES—INTERMEDIATE IV

1. J. M. Poe.

2. Don Ables.

3. William Waldman, Mitchell Scibor.

4. Heinz Michaelis.

5. Allison Folsom and George Donabedian.

6. Sam Ballen.

7. Leonard Hutchison.

8. Garland Slack.

9. Gertrude Hunter and Edith Whitworth.

10. Bobby Patterson. And, of course, Bobby Patterson. One was a musician known to Ruby; the other was a police officer, and therefore most likely known to Ruby.

WARREN COMMISSION WITNESSES—EXPERT

1. How many husband-wife groups testified?

2. Name as many as you can.

3. How many of those couples never met Oswald; which ones?

4. What Secret Service agent led the Kennedy group out of Parkland, with a weapon quite obvious?

5. Whose wife was called to weaken the previously given testimony of her husband?

6. Which witness participated in a Commission time-reconstruction test which "proved" Oswald could not have reached the Tippit scene in time to be a shooter?

7. How much did busdriver McWatters indicate bus fare was?

8. What was Commander Humes' confusion about the time the autopsy ended?

9. Whose testimony reinforced this?

10. How many Warren Commission witnesses have references in their testimony to polygraph tests that were given?

Answers on next page

ANSWERS
WARREN COMMISSION WITNESSES—EXPERT

1. Sixteen husband-wife combinations testified.

2. The Fords, DeMohrenschildts, Tobiases, Paines, Connallys, Rowlands, Cabells, Mr. and Mrs. J. Evans, Mr. and Mrs. J. Hall, Mr. and Mrs. I. Voshinin, Mr. and Mrs. T. .Ray, Mr. and Mrs. A.C. Johnson, Mr. and Mrs. F. Davis, Mr. and Mrs. Homer Wood, Mr. and Mrs. Carlin, and Mr. and Mrs. Olsen. (The second to testify most often gave "me, too" testimony.)

3. Eight; Connally, Rowlands, Cabell, Voshinin, Davis, Wood, Carlin, Olsen.

4. Roy Kellerman.

5. Arnold Rowlands.

6. William Whaley.

7. Twenty-three cents.

8. Humes testified they stopped at 11 PM; later testimony mentioned the early hours of the next day.

9. Clint Hill.

10. Four.

WARREN COMMISSION WITNESSES—EXPERT II

1. Who was the Depository employee who saw Oswald leave the second floor using the staircase that led to the main exit?

2. What witness was confronted with a tape recording suggesting an earlier identification was erroneous?

3. Who made that tape recording?

4. What FBI agent was called to testify with regards to fingerprints?

5. What Dallas police officer was flown to Washington to answer eight questions about Oswald's second arraignment?

6. What FBI agent interviewed Oswald on more than one occasion when he had just returned from his "defection"?

7. What two officers from Dallas heard FBI agent Hosty suggest that the bureau had more information about Oswald than they were letting on?

8. What veterinarian testified before the Commission?

9. Who testified regarding the building of a mock-up of Dealey Plaza?

10. What second-grade classmate of Oswald's had the distinction of testifying before the Commission?

Answers on next page

ANSWERS
WARREN COMMISSION WITNESSES—EXPERT II

1. Mrs. R. Reid.

2. Helen Markham. The tape recording, played to Ms. Markham by the Commission, was of a phone call to her from an attorney. Ms. Markham insisted that the call never happened, *and* that it involved herself and a high-ranking Dallas police official.

3. Mark Lane.

4. Sebastian Latona.

5. T.L. Baker.

6. John Fain.

7. Jack Revill and V.J. Brian.

8. Dr. Alfred G. Olivier.

9. Leo J. Gauthier.

10. Philip Vinson.

WARREN COMMISSION WITNESSES—EXPERT III

1. Jack Ruby's cleaning lady gave testimony; name her.

2. Name two Cabinet members who testified before the Commission.

3. Name the head of the Passport Office who was grilled about Oswald's ease of access to a passport.

4. Name the only translator (out of several) for Marina Oswald who was required to give testimony to prove he was qualified.

5. Only one witness took the Fifth Amendment, but he did it 31 times; name the witness.

6. One person on the Triple Underpass has been identified as being neither an officer or a local railroad worker. Name him.

7. Which of Oswald's former landladies noticed him on Cecil McWatters' bus, later testifying that he looked like a wild man?

8. Who transported the "gun bag" to police headquarters?

9. Name the two men who visited Oswald with respect to legal counsel.

10. What officer found the "curb mark"?

Answers on next page

ANSWERS
WARREN COMMISSION WITNESSES—EXPERT III

1. Elnora Pitts.

2. Secretary of State Dean Rusk and Treasury Secretary Douglas Dillon. Rusk testified with respect to the immediate diplomatic reactions to the murder of JFK; Dillon, as nominal head of the Secret Service, testified to budgetary needs.

3. Frances Knight.

4. Harris Coulter.

5. Robert A. Surrey, who gave testimony about General Walker and the political climate surrounding the Walker group.

6. Royce Skelton.

7. Mary Bledsoe.

8. L.D. Montgomery.

9. Greg Olds and H. Louis Nichols. Olds represented the Dallas ACLU; Nichols was head of the Dallas Bar Association in 1963.

10. "Buddy" Walthers, with help from "victim" James Tague.

WARREN COMMISSION WITNESSES—EXPERT IV

1. Name any of the four friends from Oswald's teenage years who testified before the Commission.

2. Name the Mexican prisoner who appeared in a lineup with Oswald and subsequently testified.

3. Name the New Orleans police official who dealt with Oswald after the leaflet fracas.

4. Name the head of the Fair Play for Cuba Committee, who testified that the organization ceased functioning after the assassination.

5. Name the car salesman's boss (from the highspeed test-drive event).

6. Name the Australian girl on the Mexican bus with Oswald who gave testimony in Los Angeles.

7. Name the typist who was willing to prepare Oswald's narrative of his stay in Russia.

8. Name three young witnesses who testified and whose parent also gave testimony.

9. Name the two boys who testified to the meeting of Oswald and Carlos Bringuier in Bringuier's store.

10. Name the officer in the basement who seemed most under suspicion in Ruby's shooting of Oswald.

Answers on next page

ANSWERS
WARREN COMMISSION WITNESSES—EXPERT IV

1. Ed Voebel, William Wulf, Bennerieta Smith, and F. O'Sullivan.

2. Dan Lujan.

3. Lt. F. Martello.

4. V. T. Lee.

5. Frank Pizzo. Although he was unable to identify Oswald in photos he was shown, those photos went into the official record as "Pizzo Exhibits."

6. Pamela Mumford.

7. Pauline Bates.

8. Linda Willis, Charles Steele, Sterling Wood.

9. Philip Geraci and Vincent Blalock.

10. "Blackie" Harrison.

"HOLLYWOOD" AND THE ASSASSINATION—EXPERT

1. Name the science fiction movie in which someone returns in time to Dallas to prevent the assassination of JFK.

2. In the first trial of Oswald on television, c. late '70s, who defends Oswald?

3. Who is the prosecutor in that case?

4. How is Oswald shown in that case?

5. In the 1986 British version of the same event, who was the defense counsel?

6. Who was the prosecutor in that version?

7. How was Oswald portrayed in that version?

8. What movie was based on a book by Mark Lane?

9. In the above movie, who is hinted at as the ultimate decision making person with respect to the assassination?

10. As filmed, and later as shown, how long was the 1986 British "trial" of Oswald?

Answers on next page

ANSWERS
"HOLLYWOOD" AND THE ASSASSINATION—EXPERT

1. *A Time to Remember.*

2. Lorne Greene.

3. Ben Gazzara.

4. He is a prisoner in a glass enclosure.

5. Gerry Spence.

6. Vincent Bugliosi.

7. Oswald is presented as a photo and is on trial posthumously.

8. *Executive Action.*

9. H.L. Hunt (as played by Will Geer).

10. The original was seventeen hours long; as shown in the states, it took five hours.

JFK: THE MOVIE—BEGINNER

1. What is the phrase used when someone fires at a target on a rifle range and misses the target?

2. What secret operation is mentioned repeatedly throughout the movie?

3. What was odd about Ferrie's suicide notes?

4. The mystery chararacter who gives Garrison a great deal of covert intelligence data refers to himself by what designation?

5. By what designation does the mystery man refer to his superior officer?

6. What actor played the mystery man?

7. Who is the mystery man in real life?

8. Which son of Jim Garrison's is referred to most often?

9. What phrase does Jim Garrison repeat several times during the showing of the Zapruder film?

10. The "action" of the movie begins after JFK is nuzzled by a horse while saying "And we are all mortal," a clip from the American U. speech. Who is the next character seen?

Answers on next page

ANSWERS
JFK: THE MOVIE—BEGINNER

1. "Maggie's Drawers."

2. Operation Mongoose.

3. Both were typed and unsigned.

4. "X."

5. "General Y."

6. Donald Sutherland

7. Colonel L. Fletcher Prouty.

8. Jasper.

9. "Back and to the left..."

10. Rose Cheramie.

JFK: THE MOVIE—INTERMEDIATE

1. After footage of the motorcade is shown, when the first shot is fired, what is depicted on the screen?

2. What is the next scene?

3. What brand of cigarettes did David Ferrie ask for?

4. Whom did Ferrie call when he feared for his life?

5. Where did Garrison meet with Ferrie after the phone call?

6. With whom did Garrison take a plane ride which rekindled his interest in the JFK assassination?

7. What was the name of Garrison's dog?

8. Who was the first witness shown testifying to the Warren Commission?

9. Who indicated that her testimony before the Warren Commission was a total fabrication?

10. Who indicated that her FBI statement had been forged and wrongly notarized?

Answers on next page

ANSWERS
JFK: THE MOVIE—INTERMEDIATE

1. Pigeons flying off the TSBD.

2. A bulletin interrupting television programming.

3. Luckies.

4. Lou Ivon.

5. The Fountainbleu Hotel.

6. Senator Russell Long of Louisiana.

7. Touchdown

8. Lee Bowers.

9. Jean Hill

10. Julia Ann Mercer.

JFK: THE MOVIE—INTERMEDIATE II

1. What medicine found at Ferrie's apartment made Garrison curious?

2. What were the last words of the "mystery man"?

3. How did the other passenger on the flight describe JFK's successor?

4. Where was investigator Jack Martin interviewed by Garrison?

5. Finish the statement made by Garrison's investigator: "Once ONI ....."

6. Who was the judge at the Shaw Trial?

7. What was the company name of the men in uniform who fired from the Dal-Tex Building?

8. What real name is suggested for the mystery man's superior officer?

9. Where did the mystery man learn of JFK's death?

10. What was the peculiarity attached to Shaw's dining habits?

Answers on next page

ANSWERS
JFK: THE MOVIE—INTERMEDIATE II

1. Prolaud.

2. "I hope you catch a break."

3. "That polecat Lyndon..."

4. At a racetrack.

5. "Always ONI." (Recall that JFK had served in ONI before PT-109...)

6. Edward E. Haggerty.

7. Acme Air Conditioning.

8. General Landsdale.

9. In Christchurch, New Zealand.

10. He liked to sit at one end of a long table and have his guest at the other end.

JFK: THE MOVIE—EXPERT

1. What was Guy Banister's theory on Oswald's participation in the assassination?

2. Give two reasons cited why Ferrie and his companions were able to shoot no geese.

3. What communication event did Lee Bowers testify to?

4. When Willie O'Keefe first had dinner with Clay Shaw, Shaw told him, "I hope you like (the dinner)." Name the main course.

5. Shaw had a "colored" man-servant. Give both his names.

6. How did Shaw describe JFK in his interview in Garrison's office?

7. What prominent assassination researcher was shown in Parkland Hospital scenes as well as running the projector showing the Zapruder film?

8. Who was the New Orleans coroner with whom Garrison discussed Ferrie's death?

9. Which memo did the mystery man tell of when insisting that JFK was ordering 1,000 troops to be removed from Viet Nam?

10. Who was the military commander who protested that his unit was ordered to stand down and not protect Kennedy?

Answers on next page

ANSWERS
JFK: THE MOVIE—EXPERT

1. "Oswald must have flipped."

2. No shotguns; and the geese were "a wise bunch of birds."

3. He saw a man in a vehicle with a microphone up to his mouth.

4. Squab.

5. Frankie Jenkins; "Smedley."

6. "A man of true panache."

7. Robert Groden. Based on his extensive study of the photographic material on the assassination, he had been serving as a consultant to Director Oliver Stone.

8. "Nick" in the movie. Dr. Nicholas Chetta.

9. NSAM 263.

10. Colonel Reich.

JFK: THE MOVIE—EXPERT II

1. Which three memos did the mystery man speak of when discussing JFK's removal of covert military operations from the CIA to the Joint Chiefs?

2. Which later memo, signed by LBJ, got the US deeper in Viet Nam?

3. Give Clay Shaw's address.

4. Who played a talk show host in the longer version of *JFK*?

5. According to the movie, how much did Kennedy's brain weigh?

6. Which autopsy pathologist testified to interference by higher-ups in Kennedy's autopsy?

7. Who is the only Parkland doctor to testify and be identified by name at the trial?

8. Who was the heroin addict who claimed he saw Shaw and Oswald together?

9. Garrison and his wife had a few spats during the movie; how were they resolved?

10. Where was Garrison at the time he heard of JFK's death?

Answers on next page

ANSWERS
JFK: THE MOVIE—EXPERT II

1. NSAMs 55, 56, and 57.

2. NSAM 273.

3. 1313 Dauphine Street.

4. John Larroquette.

5. 653 grams. (The recorded autopsy weight was 1500 grams, heavier than the average weight of an *intact* brain.)

6. Colonel Pierre Finck.

7. Dr. Paul Peters.

8. Vernon Bundy.

9. The Garrisons would later divorce.

10. At Napoleon's restaurant. (In fact, he was still in his office.)

JFK: THE MOVIE—"ARTISTIC LICENSE"

1. In the movie, Garrison learns of the shooting at 12:34 CST; when did he learn of it in real life?

2. In a background radio broadcast, there is an error in the name of the priest who gave the last rites. What was the error?

3. In what way does Guy Banister, in "toasting Camelot," overstate the Bay of Pigs fiasco?

4. Garrison watches a suspect, identified as Lee Oswald, being removed from a theater by the police. What is wrong with the identification?

5. What is wrong with Garrison's theory that Ferrie was a getaway pilot for Oswald?

6. What two inaccuracies exist with respect to the airplane ride in which Garrison discusses JFK with a Louisiana Senator?

7. Garrison tells that Oswald was interrogated for 12 hours without any notes being taken, suggesting that even if Oswald had said something of importance, it would be inadmissable. What is incorrect about that statement?

8. Garrison complains that an FBI man in New Orleans questioned Oswald and then destroyed his notes. What is the problem there?

9. What is inaccurate about the scene where Garrison goes to Ferrie's apartment after Ferrie's suicide?

10. Garrison's staff contend that there were no records kept regarding the tramps; what is the concern there?

Answers on next page

ANSWERS
JFK: THE MOVIE—"ARTISTIC LICENSE"

1. After JFK died.

2. Father Huber was refered to as Oscar Hubert.

3. Banister claimed thousands of Cubans were killed or tortured as a result of the Bay of Pigs.

4. It was not yet known that the suspect's name was Oswald.

5. Ferrie did not leave for Texas until after Oswald was caught.

6. The flight was to New York, so they would not have seen the White House; it is also a security violation to fly that close to the White House.

7. Under Texas law, any such statements are inadmissable regardless of whether they are taken down or not.

8. FBI agents routinely destroy notes after a report is written.

9. Ferrie's body was not present by the time Garrison got to the apartment.

10. Records of the "tramps" were kept, albeit out of the public eye for years.

JFK: THE MOVIE—"ARTISTIC LICENSE II"

1. Jean Hill describes the agonal moments of the motorcade, telling that Mary Moorman fell, but she (Jean Hill) remained standing. What is the error here?

2. Garrison tells that Julia Ann Mercer's statement to the Warren Commission had been altered. What is inaccurate in that statement?

3. Garrison missed Easter dinner with his family because of a Sunday meeting with Shaw. How is that inaccurate?

4. What phrase is used in the movie that was an unknown idiom in the 1960s?

5. The mystery man tells Garrison that "the entire Cabinet was in the Far East"; what are the inaccuracies there?

6. In the movie, Clay Shaw is arrested at his apartment; where was he actually arrested?

7. The movie's hypothesis suggests that sixth-floor Depository shooters had access to that area because flooring work was being done and there were strangers in and out. What is the error there?

8. A rifleman is depicted behind the picket fence. What is wrong with the suggested depiction?

9. Garrison claimed that when Oswald got to police headquarters, he was booked for the murder of Tippit. When was Oswald booked for that crime?

10. Garrison told his listeners at the 1969 trial of Shaw that he was in his early fourties, and that key documents would not be released until 2038 A.D. What two errors are in that statement?

Answers on next page

ANSWERS
JFK: THE MOVIE—"ARTISTIC LICENSE II"

1. Moorman is seen standing in the Zapruder film.

2. Julia Ann Mercer was not called by the Warren Commission. The statement she gave to the FBI and possibly evaluated by the WC had been altered.

3. The meeting occurred in December of 1966.

4. "Wanna-be."

5. RFK and Robert McNamara were not with the four or five Cabinet members en route to Asia.

6. In Garrison's office.

7. The flooring work was done by Depository employees.

8. The shooter was balancing the gun himself; a marksman would use the fence as a natural gunrest.

9. Five hours later.

10. Garrison was 47 at the time of the trial, and the material was sequestered until 2039 A.D.

JFK ASSASSINATION LITERATURE—BEGINNER
(NAME AUTHOR/ TITLE)

1. JFK's body was "altered" between Parkland Hospital and Bethesda Naval Hospital.

2. Marita Lorenz's testimony caused E. Howard Hunt to lose a lawsuit, and also suggested his complicity in the assassination.

3. Based on documents available in the mid-1960s, the Warren Commission's methodologies were quite poor.

4. An author suggested in several early volumes that the JFK assassination was a government cover-up.

5. An early Texas researcher who published several volumes which, among other things, took note of the many strange deaths in the case.

6. A well-researched book suggested that Oswald performed the assassination alone, and that there were many parallels to the Lincoln case.

7. A biography of Oswald insisting he was the one and only assassin.

8. An early work that suggested the government investigation was conducted in haste.

9. A recent work that suggested conspiracy, but it only involved Oswald.

10. A recent work that suggested that Oswald could not have been convicted in a courtroom.

Answers on next page

ANSWERS
JFK ASSASSINATION LITERATURE—BEGINNER

1. Lifton, *Best Evidence*.

2. Lane, *Plausible Denial*.

3. Epstein, *Inquest*.

4. Weisberg, *Whitewash* series.

5. Jones, *Forgive My Grief*.

6. Lattimer, *Kennedy and Lincoln*.

7. Ford (with J.R. Stiles), *Portrait of the Assassin*.

8. Lane, *Rush to Judgement*.

9. Moore, *Conspiracy of One*.

10. Brown, *People v. Lee Harvey Oswald*.

JFK ASSASSINATION LITERATURE—INTERMEDIATE

1. A district attorney wrote two non-fiction works on the assassination.

2. A book suggesting that Oswald had a cover-story built around him.

3. Two books that suggested Lee Oswald had been "substituted" at some point, hinting that the "real Oswald" had nothing to do with the crime.

4. The first work devoted solely to Oswald imposters.

5. The book that claimed to have found the mysterious "Saul."

6. A work by a philosophy professor that indicated that the ballistics and timing suggested by the Warren Commission were incorrect.

7. A book which indicated a Secret Service agent in the follow-up car killed JFK.

8. A work which pointed the finger of blame directly at Lyndon Johnson.

9. The only published work by a Parkland Doctor.

10. The most recent work published by the man portrayed by Donald Sutherland in *JFK*.

Answers on next page

ANSWERS
JFK ASSASSINATION LITERATURE—INTERMEDIATE

1. Jim Garrison, *Heritage of Stone, On the Trail of the Assassins*.

2. Epstein, *Legend*.

3. Cutler, *Alias Oswald*; Eddowes, *The Oswald File*.

4. Richard Popkin, *The Second Oswald*.

5. McDonald, *Appointment in Dallas*.

6. Thompson, *Six Seconds in Dallas*.

7. Meninger, *Mortal Error*.

8. Zirbel, *The Texas Connection*.

9. Crenshaw, *Conspiracy of Silence*.

10. Prouty, *JFK*.

JFK ASSASSINATION LITERATURE—EXPERT

1. The only book published by a Secret Service agent in the motorcade.

2. Published in England, it was one of the first two books critical of the official version, appearing even before *The Warren Report*.

3. Published in England, it was the other of the first two critical books, and it is difficult to get today, as rumors persist that the original limited printing was bought up by the U.S. Embassy in London.

4. A satirical play suggesting LBJ's complicity.

5. A work with three bullet holes through the cover.

6. The first assassination-related book written by "Mr. X" from *JFK*.

7. The memoirs, published posthumously, of the Commission's best eyewitness.

8. A difficult book to obtain, it was written as a memoir by a high-ranking Dallas police official.

9. A book that used a psychological stress evaluator to indicate who was telling the truth and who was lying in the JFK case.

10. A book by a previously published researcher that found very little merit in Jim Garrison's case.

Answers on next page

ANSWERS
JFK ASSASSINATION LITERATURE—EXPERT

1. Rufus Youngblood, *Twenty Years in the Secret Service*.

2. Buchanan, *Who Killed Kennedy?*

3. Gun, *Red Roses of Dallas*.

4. Barbara Garson, *Macbird*.

5. Fox, *Unanswered Questions about the Kennedy Assassination*.

6. Prouty, *The Secret Team*.

7. Brennan, *Eyewitness to History*.

8. Curry, *Memoirs*.

9. O'Toole, *The Assassination Tapes*.

10. Epstein, *Counterplot*.

ASSASSINATION FICTION—INTERMEDIATE

(MATCHING)

1. *The Double Man*　　　　　　A. Wesley Thurston

2. *Libra*　　　　　　　　　　B. Jim Garrison

3. *Betrayal*　　　　　　　　　C. George Bernau

4. *Oswald's Game*　　　　　　D. Charles McCarry

5. *Star Spangled Contract*　　　E. Robert Mayer

6. *I, JFK.*　　　　　　　　　　F. Stanley Shapiro

7. *The Trumpets of November*　　G. Senators Cohen and Hart

8. *A Time to Remember*　　　　H. Don Delillo

9. *Promises to Keep*　　　　　　I. Robert Morrow

10. *The Tears of Autumn*　　　　J. Jean Davison

Answers on next page

ANSWERS
ASSASSINATION FICTION—INTERMEDIATE

1. G.

2. H.

3. I.

4. J.

5. B.

6. E.

7. A.

8. F.

9. C.

10. D.

ASSASSINS—INTERMEDIATE

1. The CIA took a photo of someone—not Lee Oswald—leaving either the Cuban or Russian Embassy in Mexico City. According to one researcher the subject of the photo was JFK's real killer. Give the name cited by the researcher.

2. A self-proclaimed U.S. intelligence agent was approached by KGB elements to kill Lee Oswald before the assassination. The man in question arranged for himself to be jailed before the assassination.

3. Name the individual arrested in Chicago in November, 1963 because of a threat he posed to President Kennedy.

4. Of all the "theories" concerning assassins, who were the three closest assassins to JFK?

5. What rogue CIA agent, who later "murdered" his parents and disappeared, is said to be "the man on the knoll"?

6. From what other building have shots been suspected?

7. What professional hit man, now serving a long stretch, has often been a suspect in the JFK case, perhaps even as the tall tramp?

8. What is the nickname given to a figure wearing what is seen as a police uniform on the knoll?

9. In an early work by Thomas Buchanan, Oswald was seen as having an accomplice on the south end of the overpass. Name him.

10. Which theoretical "assassin" allegedly fired the most shots?

Answers on next page

ANSWERS
ASSASSINS—INTERMEDIATE

1. "Saul."

2. Richard Case Nagell.

3. Thomas Vallee.

4. William Greer, the limousine driver; George Hickey, Secret Service man in the follow-up car, and the "Umbrella Man," adjacent to the road sign in the Zapruder film.

5. Charles Rogers.

6. The Dal-Tex Building, as well as the County Jail.

7. Charles Harrelson.

8. "Badgeman".

9. Jack Ruby.

10. "The Man in Black", so theory has it, fired two automatic pistols and wounded over a dozen people. This absurdity was posited by George C. Thomson, who insists that 22 shots were fired, but that JFK survived.

QUOTABLE "QUOTES" I

(WHO MADE THE FOLLOWING PARAPHRASED STATEMENTS?)

1. So we ask the citizens of Dallas to be on their best behavior...

2. We will soon launch the biggest payroll into space...excuse me, the biggest payload...it is the biggest payroll, though.

3. You can't say Dallas doesn't love you...

4. Mr. President, over here, Mr. President... (clue: a famous witness).

5. My God, they are going to kill us all...

6. Get us out of here, we are hit...

7. Pull all my available men and put them into the railroad yards...

8. Get a man up there on the overpass and see what happened...

9. It takes her a little longer, but it's worth it.

10. There is no doubt in my mind that he [Oswald] would have been found guilty beyond a reasonable doubt and to a moral certainty.

Answers on next page

ANSWERS
QUOTABLE "QUOTES" I

1. Police Chief Jesse Curry.

2. JFK in Houston, Texas.

3. Mrs. Connally, less than one minute before the shooting. The exchange is captured in a photo taken about midway on Houston Street, as JFK leans forward and cocks an ear to hear Mrs. Connally's comment.

4. Jean Hill.

5. Governor Connally.

6. S/A Roy Kellerman, in JFK's car.

7. Sheriff Bill Decker.

8. Chief Curry.

9. JFK, at a breakfast in Fort Worth on November 22, referring to Mrs. Kennedy.

10. Dallas D.A. Henry Wade.

QUOTABLE "QUOTES" II

1. Nobody cares what Lyndon and I wear...

2. No. I want everybody to see what they have done.

3. For your information, Mr. Director, the President is dead.

4. You must let us get the President inside...

5. I know now and I have always known that I was hit with the second shot; there's no doubt about that.

6. I am not resisting arrest...

7. We were expecting you. Please come in....

8. I absolve you of all sins, in the name of the Father, the Son, and the Holy Spirit, Amen...

9. The President is dead, Mr. President...

10. We have a flash just in from Dallas. President Kennedy died at 1 pm Central Time, some 38 minutes ago. That is official...

Answers on next page

ANSWERS
QUOTABLE "QUOTES" II

1. JFK, on the morning of November 22, when Mrs. Kennedy took a little longer to get ready.

2. Mrs. Kennedy, refusing to change her blood-stained garments.

3. Robert Kennedy, telling J.E. Hoover that JFK was dead.

4. S/A Clint Hill, trying to overcome Mrs. Kennedy's unwillingness to let go of JFK upon arrival at Parkland.

5. Governor John Connally.

6. Lee Harvey Oswald.

7. Mrs. Paine, allowing the search of her home on November 22.

8. Father Oscar Huber.

9. Ken O'Donnell, passing the news of Kennedy's death to LBJ.

10. Walter Cronkite.

QUOTABLE "QUOTES" III

1. You're the police...you figure it out...

2. I hope if there is someone out there, that they can't shoot as well as you can...

3. No. But if you come to the White House on Monday, I'll put it on for you there.

4. Do you think I should close my clubs?

5. I understand that; but with respect to Texas law, this is just another homicide...

6. I know this: we'll carry at least two states next fall—Massachusetts and Texas.

7. We thought it odd...him parading around the barracks talking Russian, and nobody said a word about it...

8. I struck a policeman...

9. They told me they had three shots and three bullets, and I was not to say anything else.

10. I ask for your help, and God's...

Answers on next page

ANSWERS
QUOTABLE "QUOTES" III

1. Lee Oswald/Alek Hidell, in custody.

2. Detective Jim Leavelle, to Oswald, just before the transfer in which Oswald was shot.

3. JFK, regarding a cowboy hat he had been given, but would not wear on camera in Texas.

4. Jack Ruby, according to Seth Kantor.

5. Dr. Earl Rose, Dallas coroner.

6. JFK, to LBJ's sister on the morning of November 22.

7. Any of Oswald's marine buddies.

8. Lee Oswald, on explaining how he sustained bruises.

9. Jean Hill.

10. LBJ, upon arrival at Andrews Air Force Base.

QUOTABLE "QUOTES" IV

1. My son is an agent...

2. Facts convince me that Lee killed the President.

3. Do not draw any conclusions on the so-called evidence.

4. I wanted to shoot the *S.O.B.* three times...

5. It hit so hard that I thought for a moment that I had been shot...

6. They killed him, they killed him,...

7. I definitely saw smoke come out from under those trees...

8. This is it...

9. If you want to hear from me, you'll have to get me to Washington. Can you do that?

10. That is my face, but that is not me...

Answers on next page

ANSWERS
QUOTABLE "QUOTES" IV

1. Mrs. Marguerite Oswald.

2. Marina Oswald.

3. Lee Oswald, speaking in custody to his brother Robert.

4. Jack Ruby, regarding his successful attempt on Oswald.

5. Motorcycle Officer Bobby Hargis, with respect to the human debris that hit him and his motorcycle windshield.

6. Abraham Zapruder.

7. S M. Holland.

8. Oswald, as he was being arrested.

9. Jack Ruby.

10. Oswald, when shown the backyard photos.

POTPOURRI I

(NO "DIFFICULTY" RATING)

1. What specific food did Oswald get very tired of eating while in Russia?

2. What was Rose Cheramie's real name?

3. What two major characters in the Kennedy assassination were each able to speak five languages?

4. Who co-authored the *JFK* screenplay?

5. At what location did an "Oswald" consider the purchase of trucks while the real "Oswald" was in the Soviet Union?

6. At which four locations did Oswald work (excluding U.S. government sites) after his return to America?

7. Oswald only quit one of those jobs—which one?

8. At whose urging did Oswald quit that job?

9. How long did John Kennedy receive a Presidential salary after the shots were fired in Dealey Plaza?

10. What prominent building in New Orleans was Clay Shaw associated with?

Answers on next page

ANSWERS
POTPOURRI I

1. Cabbage.

2. Melba Christine Mercades.

3. David Ferrie and George DeMohrenschildt; if you answered Mrs. Kennedy, the languages would be correct, but she has never been seen as a suspect in the assassination (not yet at least).

4. Oliver Stone and Zachary Sklar.

5. Bolton Ford in New Orleans.

6. Leslie Welding, Jaggers-Chiles-Stovall, William B. Reily Coffee, and the Texas School Book Depository.

7. Leslie Welding.

8. George DeMohrenschildt, seen as instrumental in Oswald obtaining the job at Jaggers-Chiles-Stovall, where highly sensitive intelligence work was done.

9. Kennedy's salary expired at the time he was pronounced dead, which has been generalized to approximately 1 PM in Dallas, or 2 PM in Washington, DC.

10. The New Orleans Trade Mart.

POTPOURRI II
(NO "DIFFICULTY" RATING)

1. Which major characters—husband and wife—have their names changed in the movie *JFK*?

2. What rock star/Rhodes scholar once starred in a fictional Kennedy assassination movie?

3. What alternative had been considered instead of the Dallas motorcade as proposed?

4. Where were the garments worn by John Connally stored before they entered the investigation as evidence?

5. What movie star's name appeared on the marquee in the theater where Oswald was arrested?

6. How long was Kennedy's final plane ride in life?

7. Who was the pilot of Air Force One during most of Kennedy's presidency?

8. What American, Ambassador to South Viet Nam, met with LBJ to help rethink our commitment to Southeast Asia before JFK was even buried?

9. How many U.S. Presidents were alive on the day of JFK's funeral?

10. When was the last documented assassination attempt of a U.S. President prior to JFK's term?

Answers on next page

ANSWERS
POTPOURRI II

1. Ruth and Michael Paine become the Williams family. Michael Paine is given brief exposure in the uncut *JFK,* and the same actor appears as a spectator at the trial in the standard version of the movie.

2. Kris Kristofferson.

3. A proposed alternative was that JFK be driven from Fort Worth, west of Dallas, to the Trade Mart, on the western edge of Dallas; instead, the Presidential party flew to Love Field and took the tragic motorcade through Dallas.

4. In the closet of Congressman Henry Gonzalez (D-Texas) office, and they were laundered before being received as evidence, rendering them useless.

5. Van Heflin.

6. Thirteen minutes — Fort Worth to Dallas.

7. Colonel Jim Swindal.

8. Henry Cabot Lodge, whom Kennedy had defeated in a 1952 Senate race, and who had been Nixon's running mate in 1960. This is not to suggest a connection...

9. Four: Herbert Hoover (d. 1964), Harry S. Truman (d. 1972), Dwight D. Eisenhower (d. 1969), and, of course, LBJ. (Six, and possibly more, future Presidents were alive that day, although Bill Clinton was a teenager.)

10. November 1, 1950 — at Blair House, while the White House was being gutted; Harry S Truman was the target. At least one White House guard was killed; one of the two assailants was also killed.

POTPOURRI III

(NO "DIFFICULTY" RATING)

1. On November 22, 1963, who would have been the last Vice-President to die in office?

2. Who were the two Secret Service Agents assigned to guard Air Force One, and what "off-the-record" events were they involved in after the shooting of the President?

3. What literary figure's death was reported on November 22, although usually on page 19 because the news from Dallas took up the rest of the paper?

4. Who was the City Manager of Dallas on November 22, 1963?

5. Where was Michael Paine employed?

6. Who was Michael Paine's father?

7. What did Michael Paine believe was in the "Oswald blanket" in his garage?

8. Who took control of the Justice Department during Robert Kennedy's absence following the assassination?

9. For what group did Kennedy have the Dallas motorcade stop?

10. What deaf mute witnessed serious events with respect to the assassination, but was ignored by the FBI and Warren Commission?

Answers on next page

ANSWERS
POTPOURRI III

1. James T. Sherman, in 1912, and he was the seventh Vice President to die in office (G. Clinton, E. Gerry, W. King, H. Wilson, T. Hendricks, G. Hobart were the others). As of this writing, no more have, and none of the seven listed were assassinated.

2. Roger Warner and James T. Howard; Warner left his post to interview a suspect arrested in Forth Worth, and Howard would later tell Thayer Waldo, a reporter, that the Warren Commission had an African-American eyewitness who saw Oswald pull the trigger from a vantage point a few feet away; nothing more was ever heard of these events.

3. Aldous Huxley.

4. Elgin Crull.

5. Bell Helicopter, manufacturer of the Vietnam workhorse helicopter.

6. George L. Paine, a leader of the Trotskyite movement in the U.S.

7. Camping equipment; he stated he felt the contents and it seemed like tent poles and/or a small shovel.

8. Nicholas deB. Katzenbach.

9. For a group of nuns, and for a group that had a placard, "Stop and shake our hands."

10. Ed Hoffman, who is still active in research into the events of November 22.

POTPOURRI IV
(NO "DIFFICULTY" RATING)

1. Name the two Cuban consular officials who dealt with "Oswald" in Mexico City.

2. What American intelligence operative, linked to the late Oleg Penkovsky, gave the Oswalds their physicals before they left the Soviet Union in 1962?

3. Who met the Oswald family upon their return from the Soviet Union?

4. Who were Guy Banister's two secretaries?

5. Who drove the ambulance which bore the epileptic from Dealey Plaza and which, an hour later, delivered a coffin to Parkland Hospital?

6. Who was issued the Mexican tourist card immediately ahead of Lee Oswald?

7. Who was the official White House photographer in the motorcade?

8. What citizen used Tippit's radio to call in the emergency at that location?

9. Who was the key witness in General Walker's neighborhood on April 10, 1963?

10. Who found the bone fragment in Dealey Plaza on November 23, 1963?

Answers on next page

ANSWERS
POTPOURRI IV

1. Sylvia Duran and Eusebio Azcue.

2. Captain Alexis Davidson. Davidson had family in Atlanta, where
   the Oswalds stopped briefly on their way to Texas, causing some
   "intelligence-related" speculation.

3. Spas T. Raikin.

4. Delphine Roberts and Mary Brengel.

5. Aubrey Rike.

6. William Gaudet, a CIA operative.

7. Thomas Atkins. He was located well back, however, rendering him useless.

8. T.F. Bowley.

9. Walter Kirk Coleman. Though not called by the Commission, he told
   Dallas investigators that he saw suspicious individuals drive away in
   two vehicles.

10. William Allen Harper, hence its name, "the Harper fragment." Oddly, it
    was only taken to Southern Methodist Hospital on Saturday, November
    23, after the President's skull had been virtually reconstructed at the
    autopsy on November 22.

POTPOURRI V

(NO "DIFFICULTY" RATING)

1. Who was the Chicago Secret Service Agent who found himself in serious difficulties for revealing the threats against JFK that had existed in November, 1963?

2. Who was so concerned about a plot against JFK in late 1963 that he fired a bullet into the wall of a bank to guarantee his own arrest?

3. What happened to the individual in question 2?

4. What is our best source material for that individual?

5. Who was the high-level CIA operative often seen as being the mysterious "Maurice Bishop"?

6. With what well-known Cuban exile leader did "Maurice Bishop" have extensive dealings?

7. How does Garrison's investigator Lou Ivon describe the Mannlicher-Carcano when he and Garrison are shown on the sixth floor of the TSBD in *JFK*?

8. How high from the floor is the bottom of the "sniper window" in the TSBD?

9. What two "punitive" personal actions were taken against Jim Garrison during his investigation of Clay Shaw?

10. Which of Garrison's assistants actually asked Colonel Finck, during the Clay Shaw trial, exactly who was giving the orders at the President's autopsy?

Answers on next page

ANSWERS
POTPOURRI V

1. Special Agent Abraham Bolden.

2. Richard Case Nagell.

3. He was arrested, convicted, and given a lengthy sentence in Federal prison; it was commuted after five years, as it was seen that the prisoner was mentally incompetent (a designation common to those who disagree with the official version of the events of November 22).

4. A book by Dick Russell, *The Man Who Knew Too Much*.

5. David Atlee Phillips.

6. Antonio Veciana.

7. "The world's worst shoulder weapon."

8. Thirteen inches.

9. His taxes were audited and he was asked to resign from his reserve unit in the military.

10. Alvin Oser.

LINGERING DOUBTS/UNANSWERED QUESTIONS

1. Who pulled the trigger(s) that killed JFK?

2. Why was it done?

3. What was Oswald's involvement?

4. Why did the Kennedy family accept the official verdict without question?

5. Why was the autopsy such a disgrace?

6. Why, if Oswald the killer died so quickly, was so much material destroyed, sanitized, or sequestered?

7. Can a coverup as large as suggested by some researchers really exist and succeed?

8. What would Hoover have done with his secret files if JFK had sacked him?

9. How would Vietnam be written in history if JFK had lived?

10. When will we know the whole story?

**Answers "available" from the U.S. government—
when they decide to release them.**

D.

t

f

Lucy Robbins Welles Library
95 Cedar Street
Newington, CT 06111